M000168532

LOS ALAMOS

beginning of an era 1943-1945

This is the story of one of the greatest scientific achievements of all time. It is the story of the founding of the Los Alamos National Laboratory and its successful secret mission to create the first atomic bomb, the weapon that ended World War II.

Information for this story was compiled and edited from previously published articles and brochures on Los Alamos history written by the staff of LANL's Public Relations Office.

ISBN 0-941232-07-7
Reprinted in 1986 under the auspices of the
Los Alamos Historical Society, P.O. Box 43, Los Alamos, NM 87544
Fifth printing 1997

starting point

military & scientific realities of 1943

Military considerations had governed the decision, by 1943, that an atomic bomb was desirable, as a means for bringing World War II to an end. Scientific considerations had governed the decision that an atomic bomb was probably feasible. Technological considerations (already being worried about, though they were almost entirely in the realm of the unknown) had made it obvious that the atomic bomb would not be built in a day or a month or a year.

The military picture was grim. The USA was at war with Japan, Germany, and Italy. American naval power had not yet recovered from the disaster at Pearl Harbor. The Japanese had conquered the Philippines, and Japanese naval power was at its height. American soldiers were heavily engaged in North Africa and elsewhere. The Germans had barely begun to suffer the reverses that would turn the tide of war against them. (They surrendered El Alamein late in 1942 and Stalingrad in 1943.) German scientists were working—no American knew how ineffectively—toward an atomic bomb.

The scientific picture was exciting. The phenomenon of uranium fission had been observed several years earlier and had been correctly interpreted before 1940. It was known that at least one kind of uranium nucleus would divide (roughly in half) upon absorption of a neutron, and that this reaction liberated energy plus more neutrons. In December, 1942, a Chicago group under Enrico Fermi had succeeded in bringing about the world's first man-made nuclear chain reaction—a reaction in which the neutrons from fission caused further fission at a sustained level.

The technological picture was very nearly a blank, so far as atomic bombs were concerned. This was true not only because no one had ever tried to build an atomic bomb, but because so much fundamental scientific research remained to be done before anyone ever could.

Enough was known already to suggest the magnitude of the task, both scientifically and technologically. It was known, for instance, that the essential fissionable material—the heart of the bomb—would be hard to prepare.

Fermi's historic "pile" consisted of graphite

The military picture was grim in 1943. Right: Anti-aircraft gunners on USS Sangamon fight off burning Japanese Kamikaze plane. Opposite: As one American scout falls in Italy, his comrades dart into a doorway for temporary shelter from the barrage.

blocks and lumps of natural uranium. Natural uranium is more than 99% U-238, a heavy isotope unfit for use in a bomb because of its tendency to capture neutrons without fissioning. Uranium-235, the lighter isotope needed for a weapon, makes up about seven-tenths of one per cent of naturally-occurring uranium. Separating U-235 from the more abundant isotopes is extremely difficult, since the chemical behavior of the two isotopes offers no differences great enough to form the basis of an efficient chemical separation process.

Slight differences in physical behavior include the fact that atoms of U-235 diffuse through porous material at a somewhat faster rate than atoms of U-238, and also the fact that the trajectory of a fast-moving U-235 ion (an atom lacking one or more of its natural electrons) will bend slightly more, in a given transverse magnetic field, than the trajectory of any accompanying ions of U-238. Both of these slight behavioral differences (as well as others, even less promising) were under intensive study by 1941.

In 1943 a separation plant based on the different diffusion rates was built at Oak Ridge, Tennessee, to produce enriched uranium (uranium containing more than the natural proportion of U-235) for possible use in a weapon. At the time of the founding of the Los Alamos Laboratory, construction of the Tennessee plant had not yet begun. There was not enough enriched uranium in the world for a single bomb, or even for satisfactory laboratory investigations of U-235 behavior. Material for the first uranium bomb would not be ready for more than a year.

Minute quantities of a second fissionable element, plutonium, had been created at Berkeley in the winter of 1940-41. Plutonium does not occur in nature, but can be formed from uranium-238 through a complicated series of events beginning with the capture of neutrons by the uranium. The construction of nuclear reactors to furnish neutrons for this process began in 1943 at Oak Ridge, Tennessee (on a small scale) and Hanford, Washington (on a large scale). At the time of the founding of Los Alamos Laboratory, all the world's plutonium could still have been piled on a pinhead, with room to spare.

Thus in January, 1943, not only was there no fissionable material for bomb-making; construction of the Tennessee and Washington plants from which the material would come had not even begun.

Methods of devising a bomb deriving its explosive energy from the fission of U-235 or Pu-239 were purely speculative. The engineering effort was entirely in the future, and it would depend heavily on the results of physical, chemical, and metallurgical studies of the two possible core materials. These studies would have to be made on extremely small quantities of uranium and plutonium, so that the necessary knowledge would be gained by the time larger quantities should become available.

Thus it was that the Los Alamos Laboratory, or Project Y as it was called, became the crucial part of a super-secret nationwide research and development program known as the Manhattan Engineer District of the War Department. While other groups worked toward development and production of materials, the mission of the Laboratory, under the direction of J. Robert Oppenheimer, was to perform the necessary research, develop the technology and then to produce the actual bombs in time to affect the outcome of the war. The story of how this was done, in the face of the problems just suggested and other problems soon to be encountered, has already become a classic of science and engineering. It begins with the choice of a site for the laboratory that was to become, in the words of Dr. I. I. Rabi, "the first line of defense of the United States."

As the following chapter will show, geology and geography played a remote but finite part in the selection of the location on the Pajarito Plateau in New Mexico's Jemez Mountains—an isolated school for boys with "adequate quarters for the 30 scientists" who were all the project would need, or so the founding fathers thought.

the place

Early map makers, looking at the rectangular block of the Jemez Mountain range in northern New Mexico, apparently noted with only passing interest the circular shape formed by a series of peaks near the center.

The great circle, if they noted it at all, must have appeared to them to be merely a curious set of connected mountain valleys, 8,500 feet above sea level, separated by conical hills ranging in size from knobs to 11,000-foot mountains. On their maps they gave these lovely alpine valleys their collective Spanish name: Los Valles del Monte. The eastern rim of the circular range, overlooking present-day Los Alamos, still bears the name of Sierra de los Valles. Early geological reports refer to the region as "the Valles Mountain volcanic center," or something equally non-committal.

It was not until sometime in the 1920's that the idea that this unusual geographic feature might actually be the rim of an ancient and extinct volcano began to gain acceptance. There never was any question of the volcanic origin of the Jemez range. Even to the untrained eye thick layers of volcanic ash, heaps of burned rock, cone-shaped hills and fumeroles, and bubbling hot sulfur springs, all give unmistakable evidence of an open passage to the underworld in the not-too-distant past.

The Indian name "Jemez" means "Place of the Boiling Springs."

Relief maps and aerial photography clearly said that here was once a huge volcano, but only served to start another argument. One group of geologists claimed the big hole really was a crater, the top of a volcano. If this were true, it would be the largest known in the world, some 50 miles around and encompassing nearly 200 square miles. The other group insisted it was a caldera, the huge saucer left when a volcano collapses upon itself after having spewed all its insides out. There are lots of big calderas, some even bigger than this one. Clarence S. Ross of the U.S. Geological Survey, who has devoted 30 years to studying this region, is now certain it is a caldera.

The caldera and the surrounding peaks are the final result of a series of upheavals dating back perhaps ten million years and continuing down to a few tens of thousands of years ago. Cone-shaped peaks of varied size rising within the caldera, including 11,250-foot Redondo Peak, are known to

be secondary volcanic upthrusts. They came into existence after the original volcano collapsed to form the great basin. The basin itself once was a lake which left wave terraces visible today along the high rim. Ages ago the lake cut through the rim and drained away down what is now the Jemez river gorge.

The lush, grassy valleys between the secondary peaks inside the basin have Spanish names, like most places in New Mexico—Valle Grande, Valle Jaramillo, Valle de los Posos, Valle Santa Rosa, Valle San Antonio. One of the valleys, the Valle Grande, is best known because it is the only one alongside a public road, State Highway 4. It is the largest valley in the group, but it is only a fraction of the caldera. However, its name often appears on maps and is popularly ascribed to the entire basin. The error probably will stick.

The error is understandable. The Valle Grande itself is huge enough, a vast sea of grass on which great herds of cattle and sheep appear as ants. Intermediate forested hills block the view of distant adjoining valleys, so that only from an airplane up 15,000 feet or more is it possible to see the whole caldera. In winter, when the main peaks stand starkly around the blanket of snow that fills the valleys, the circular shape is particularly evident from the air. But planes have been flying over the range only a short time—actually since World War II. The place names were established long before people could view the whole magnificent panorama. So if you call it all the Valle Grande, not many will argue the point.

In the 1880's the Valle Grande was used for maneuvers by soldiers from Santa Fe's Fort Marcy, who built a log fort on East Jemez Creek. Navajo hogans were standing along a ridge bordering Valle Toledo, in the northeast section, until recent times. Apaches and Utes also passed this way in ancient times.

Somewhere in this period also a sawyer named Buckman started a mill, one of several in the region, and hauled lumber to the narrow-gauge railroad station across the Rio Grande from White Rock at what came to be known as Buckman's station. Logging operations have continued off and on down to the present-day in the caldera and around it.

High altitude view shows rugged canyon-pierced Pajarito Plateau below the rim of the Jemez Caldera; part of the Valle Grande is visible upper right.

The Valle Grande, part of a giant volcanic caldera in the Jemez Mountains is 8,500 feet above sea level.

Next to the great Jemez caldera, the Valle Grande, and the high peaks, probably the most prominent geological feature of the region is the long, narrow plateau that extends along and halfway up the eastern slope of the Jemez range, overlooking the Rio Grande.

Edgar L. Hewett, early-day archaeologist, named it Pajarito (Little Bird) Plateau. Lying at an altitude of between 6,300 and 7,300 feet above sea level, this wooded, volcanic bench averages a mile or two or three in width. It is severely indented along its eastern edge by a series of deep vertical canyons, where multi-colored layers of volcanic deposits are exposed by erosion. Backed up against 10,000-foot peaks, the plateau is covered thickly with pinons, juniper, and many varieties of scrub on its lower slopes, and with ponderosa pine, fir, spruce, oak, and aspen on its upper levels. It supports numerous small streams, a few of which are permanent. The few clearings are man-made.

Nomads probably wandered over the plateau for centuries, as they did along the Rio Grande, but they left no dates. There is no way yet to date with any precision the countless petroglyphs that decorate the rocks of the region. Most of these crude symbols are associated with adjacent ruins, which can be dated somewhat by tree rings and by pottery and other relics. Other "picture rocks" are near nothing and seemingly relate to nothing. They could be of any age.

At Bandelier and at Puye, Tsirege, Tsiping, and Tsankawi, from Abiquiu to Cochiti, south-facing cliffs and adjoining mesa tops are the sites of countless ruins. It is difficult for a trained observer to get out of sight of a telltale mound or cliff-opening that speaks of early Pueblo occupancy, anywhere along the length of the plateau. Pottery sherds and obsidian flakes literally pave the ground in many places. (In central Los Alamos, between the shopping center and the Lodge, a fenced area encloses a partially excavated ruin of the 12th century, black-on-white pottery period, believed to be associated with the large Otowi Pueblo ruin in Pueblo Canyon. Local archaeologists plan to restore the ruin as a public museum.)

There is no visible evidence in all these memorabilia, however, of any residence on the plateau prior to about 1150 A.D. Between that time and the Spanish occupation, many thousands of Indians evidently lived and died on the plateau, farming the valleys by day for squash and beans and corn, retreating by night to the relative security of their cliff dwellings. They were harrassed by Apaches from the south, Navajos and Utes from the north, Comanches from the east, and by a changing climate. About the only factor in their favor was the ease of digging holes in the soft pumice cliffs for storerooms behind their talus dwellings. Housing was cheap and plentiful and natural defenses were at hand. Nothing else could have been easy.

Indians existed here, in some fashion, for perhaps four hundred years, when drought apparently drove them to the Rio Grande bottom lands. They arrived just in time to meet the Spanish Conquistadores, who jerked them in short order from stone age freedom to slavery and near-extermination. Had they known what was in store for them, probably they would have stayed in the hills and starved.

Some caves along lower Frijoles creek in Bandelier National Monument are believed to have been a refuge, perhaps as late as 1700, for Indians fleeing the returning Spaniards after the Pueblo revolt of 1680. But after that there is a blank in the history of the whole Pajarito Plateau, until the arrival of the first homesteaders in the late 1880's.

(At Puye Cliffs, on the Santa Clara Indian reservation, Indians from the nearby Pueblo celebrate annually a fiesta at the site of a partially restored ruin which they insist is their ancient homesite. But the celebration is obviously just good clean fun, as it is of very recent origin. The Santa Clara Indians also maintain picnic, fishing, and recreation areas in beautiful Santa Clara Canyon.)

There can be little doubt that early hunters ventured into the forests of the Jemez for the deer, bear, elk and turkey that still abound there. Sheepherders and drovers from the haciendas of the Rio Grande valley doubtless grazed their flocks in the high meadows and in the great caldera. But they left no record that the passage of a century has not obliterated.

The mountain men of the fur trade who opened the West late in the 18th century may have trapped the Jemez streams—there are still beaver in the larger ones—but there is no mention of these mountains in their scanty journals. It is known that they trapped the Rio Grande and the Chama, and it is likely therefore that they trapped the tributaries of both.

The archaeological wonders of the plateau were first reported in the 1880's by Adolf Bandelier, for whom the present-day national monument is named,

as a result of his explorations here between 1880 and 1886. For a short time he lived with the Cochiti Indians, who claim Frijoles Canyon as one of their ancestral homes. He camped in Frijoles also, probably in one of the larger caves. From these experiences he obtained the material for his romantic historical novel "The Delight Makers," which seeks to reconstruct the lives of prehistoric dwellers in Frijoles Canyon, now headquarters for the Monument.

Not only is the archaeological record of the plateau best preserved in Bandelier National Monument, with its museum, guided tours and partially restored prehistoric dwellings, but it is also the locale for some of the earliest permanent settlements on the plateau.

A Boston judge named A. J. Abbott homesteaded Frijoles (Bean) Canyon about 1907. Abbott built a stone and log house and planted an orchard. Some of his peach trees still bloom every spring across from the upper campground.

In 1925 George and Evelyn Frey took over the place, known as Ten Elders Ranch, and started a guest ranch resort, about a quarter-mile west of the present visitor's center. They brought supplies in by cableway from the cliff top. Guests had to ride in on burro-back, down a dizzy zig-zag trail, after boarding a buckboard at Buckman on the two-day journey from Santa Fe, crossing the Rio Grande on a rickety plank bridge that washed out almost every spring. There was no road down into the canyon until 1933.

Ruins of the ancient pueblo of Tyuonyi, as well as many prehistoric cliff dwellings, are included in Bandelier National monument, 14 miles from Los Alamos.

Scene on a ranching homestead of the Pajarito Plateau, photographed before the founding of the Los Alamos Ranch School in 1917.

The old ranch buildings were torn down in 1938 by the CCC when it built the present lodge and visitor's center. Mrs. Frey, a widow, has managed the lodge since it was built.

Around Los Alamos, the earliest known occupancy was by summer bean farmers who came up from the valley. Bences Gonzales, who retired from his Laboratory employment in 1959 at the age of 66, recalls spending summers near Anchor Ranch (now GT Site) where his father had been the first settler in 1891. His wife's grandfather, Antonio Sanchez, was the first homesteader on Pajarito Mesa (above present Pajarito site) in 1885, he recalls. Some scraggly peach trees and a tumbledown log cabin are all that are left of the old ranch. Because of usually heavy snow the ranch was never occupied in the winter, Gonzales recalls.

In dry years, the farmers hauled water to the mesa top up an old trail still visible on the south side of Los Alamos canyon, just under Fire Station No. 1. It was known for years as Dead Man's Trail, because Sanchez was killed by a falling rock while building it.

The first permanent settlers in Los Alamos, who dug in for the winter with log cabins, frame houses and fireplaces, apparently arrived about 1911. The mesa was homesteaded by a man named Harold Hemingway Brook, who with a fellow lumberjack named Mack Hooper, filed on 160 acres of land each in 1911. They called it Alamos Ranch, built homes near the present Lodge building, and raised beans and wheat. Other ranchers settled on the mesas and in nearby canyons.

Alamos Ranch also was a convalescent camp, and just before the Los Alamos Ranch School opened many people who came to Santa Fe from the industrial areas of the East to recover from tuberculosis, finished up the rest cure in the pine groves of Los Alamos.

Two long-ago incidents involving water, the Southwest's most precious and unpredictable commodity, were important in the chain of events that led to the establishment of Los Alamos Ranch School.

The first occurred in 1904 in the small, foothills town of Valmora, N.M., on the east side of the Sangre de Cristo Mountains. A sudden flood washed away the buildings of a new private school, only weeks before it was to have opened.

The second was a dozen years later, more than 100 miles away in the grassy depths of Pajarito Canyon, when a stream chose to disappear suddenly.

Affected by both unrelated outbreaks of nature was a former Detroit, Mich., businessman, Ashley Pond, who possessed an unremitting determination to establish a school in New Mexico.

Pond's Valmora catastrophe, during which he carried his two-year old daughter, Peggy, to safety through the swirling waters, sent him back to Detroit until an inheritance made it possible to return.

Presence of the stream in Pajarito Canyon, colorful cliff country containing Indian reminders similar to those at nearby Frijoles, inspired Pond to choose that site for, instead of a school, a rather selective dude ranch. His Pajarito Club catered to a specific clientele, the newly affluent motorcar manufacturers of hometown Detroit, and enjoyed considerable popularity what with the abundance of hunting, fishing and exhilarating climate.

When the stream departed (investigation showed it had gone underground at the head of the canyon), Pond visited a neighbor to the north, H. H. Brook, who operated Alamos Ranch.

Pond bought out Brook's interest and incorporated at the Los Alamos Ranch School.

Pond's isolated school consisted of a conglomerate of buildings, some of rough-hewn lumber but most of logs. There was a trim main house with a circling porch much like the farmhouses of the Midwest. There was a boggy area that alternately filled and drained. Near stood a large barn. To the east, reaching almost to the tip of the mesa, was a large field that was part pasture and part cropland. West of the main buildings were service huts and cabins for the ranch hands. A dense forest of pines slipped west down a gentle slope to a 200-acre clearing that extended to the rock base of the Jemez hills. This was range land, and had barns and stables.

For director, Pond solicited the services of a forest ranger named A. J. Connell, and by January 1918, the Los Alamos Ranch School was ready for business. The first pupil, enrolled on a tutoring basis, was the son of a British consul with the unlikely but magnificent name of Lancelot Inglesby Pelly.

The school grew. Faculty members were added and new buildings went up. There was a hulking timber pile called the "Big House" to the north of the home. In 1924 another big log building was erected and named Fuller Lodge for one of the instructors, Edward J. Fuller, whose father bought a major interest in the school and helped finance it through a crucial period. It was a dining and recreation hall. Rooms upstairs were used as an infirmary and for putting up visiting parents.

A young man from Connecticut had been recruited to teach science—the first physicist on the Hill. He was Fermor Church, who married Peggy Pond a few years later.

Ashley Pond, his dream at last realized, retired to Santa Fe.

Enrollment in the school was first limited to 25, but success and expansion made it possible to accommodate 45 boys as the 1930's arrived. A six-year study program was offered. Classes were small and conducted informally.

Pond was a great believer in the vigorous life. Boys wore shorts the year round. They slept in unheated sleeping porches but had a heated interior study room in each of the residence cabins. Each lad was assigned a horse, and pack trips into the Jemez were common.

The bog at the south side of the mesa was worked over and became a 23-acre lake, a place for ice skating in the winter, for swimming and even boating in the summer. Its cracked-tufa bottom frequently sprung leaks and the water dripped away, reappearing far out on the mesa. Adobe was packed on the bottom and eventually a six-inch pipe was run two and a half miles from far up Los Alamos canyon to provide a surer water supply.

Inevitably, the pool was known as Ashley Pond.

Commencement was a spectacular outdoor affair with special guests seated on the log-columned porch. Invited Indians performed dances, then spread their craftwork on blankets for sale to the goggle-eyed visitors.

During these years an incident occurred that had great portent for the future. A visitor rode over the mesas on a pack trip. His summer home was across the valley, in the high mountains at the headwaters of the Pecos river, east of Santa Fe. His name was J. Robert Oppenheimer.

He admired the setting, and thereafter often visited the school. He remembered the place upon

Rows of crops of the Los Alamos Ranch School, growing on the site of the present Community Center. The rich volcanic soil of Los Alamos is still producing good crops of vegetables for backyard gardeners.

being confronted with a momentous decision a few years later, when he was asked to advise the Corps of Engineers on the selection of a secret laboratory site with the following specifications:

1. It had to have adequate housing for 30 scientists.

2. The land had to be owned by the government or to be easily acquired in secrecy.

3. It had to be large enough and uninhabited so as to permit safe separation of sites for experiments.

4. It had to afford easy control of access for security and safety reasons.

5. It had to have enough cleared land, free of timber, to locate the main buildings at once.

Los Alamos fitted these qualifications to a T. All the land around the school was national forest or cheap grazing land. The nearest town was 16 or 18 miles away. And it had "plenty" of housing—for 30 scientists.

Until the spring and summer of 1942, the Pajarito Plateau seemed about as far from war as was possible to get. Then, just as the annual summer program was in progress, school officials noticed a frequency of low-flying aircraft seemed to study the area. Cars and military vehicles appeared on the crest of the road that led up from the valley.

In autumn school officials were enlightened: the War Department was interested in the property. On December 7, 1942, the first anniversay of Pearl Harbor, (and five days after Fermi achieved the first nuclear chain reaction) notice was received in a brief communication from Secretary of War Stimson that the school was being taken over. The Government used condemnation proceedings but decreed all records sealed immediately. They were not released until 1961.

Parents were notified that the school was being closed, but were not told why. The Army allowed until mid-February for the property to be vacated. In a final spurt of academic fire, class work was accelerated and by the time the boys left they had completed the full year's courses and had passed New Mexico tests to prove it.

Graduation at the Los Alamos Ranch School. This building is the main part of Fuller Lodge, used as a hotel from the war years until 1966. Dancing by Indians from nearby pueblos was a feature of the exercises.

Project Y offered spartan living accommodations during the early years.

living at los alamos

The fate of the Pajarito Plateau was sealed on November 25, 1942 in an Army memo to the Commanding General of Services of Supply.

"There is a military necessity for the acquisition of this land" at Los Alamos, New Mexico, the memo said, for use as a "demolition range." The site included "approximately 54,000 acres" of which all but 8900 acres was public land supervised by the Forest Service. The Army estimated the cost of acquisition would be approximately $440,000.

Ranch School property included 27 houses, dormitories and other living quarters and 27 miscellaneous buildings valued by the Army at $246,000.

By the time the school had been notified nearly two weeks later, it had already become clear that the original estimated Project requirement of 30 scientists was ill-considered and that the Ranch School's 27 houses would be far from adequate. Therefore in December, when construction contracts were let, they included, in addition to laboratory buildings, temporary living quarters for a population of about 300 people. But even before the Ranch School students had left the Hill, construction crews had swelled the population to 1500.

On January 1, 1943 the University of California was selected to operate the new Laboratory and a formal nonprofit contract was soon drawn with the Manhattan Engineer District of the Army. By early spring, major pieces of borrowed equipment were being installed and a group of some of the finest scientific minds in the world were beginning to assemble on the Hill.

The first members of the staff were those who already had been working on related problems at the University of California under J. Robert Oppenheimer. Others came from laboratories all over the country and the world. People like Enrico Fermi, Bruno Rossi, Emelio Segre, Neils Bohr, I. I. Rabi, Hans Bethe, Rolf Landshoff, John von Neumann, Edward Teller, Otto Frisch, Joseph Kennedy, George Kistiakowsky, Richard Feynman and Edwin McMillan came to Los Alamos, some temporarily, some occasionally as consultants and others as permanent members of the staff.

Recruiting was extremely difficult. Most prospective employees were already doing important work and needed good reason to change jobs, but because of the tight security regulations, only sci-

11

In October 1943 major road improvements were underway on State Road 4 to carry heavy traffic in personnel and equipment to Los Alamos.

entific personnel could be told anything of the nature of the work to be done. These scientists were able to recognize the significance of the project and be fascinated by the challenge. The administrative people and technicians, on the other hand, were expected to accept jobs in an unknown place for an unknown purpose. Not even wives could be told where the work would take them or why.

"The notion of disappearing into the desert for an indeterminate period and under quasi-military auspices disturbed a good many scientists and the families of many more," Oppenheimer recalled later.

The wife of one of the first scientists at the Project has written: "I felt akin to the pioneer women accompanying their husbands across uncharted plains westward, alert to dangers, resigned to the fact that they journeyed, for weal or woe, into the Unknown."

But journey they did, and throughout the spring and summer of 1943 hundreds of bewildered families converged on New Mexico to begin their unforgettable adventure.

The first stop for new arrivals—civilian and military alike—was the Project's Santa Fe Office at 109 East Palace Avenue. There, under the portal of one of the oldest buildings in Santa Fe, newcomers received a warm welcome from Dorothy McKibbin who was to manage the office for twenty years.

"They arrived, those souls in transit, breathless, sleepless, haggard and tired," Mrs. McKibbin has written. "Most of the new arrivals were tense with expectancy and curiosity. They had left physics, chemistry or metallurgical laboratories, had sold their homes or rented them, had deceived their friends and launched forth to an unpredictable world."

Above: Sharp turns in the unpaved, boulder strewn road to Los Alamos made trucking of supplies a major problem. Both old and new Hill roads are visible here. Right: Ranch School buildings were quickly absorbed in the mushrooming Army construction as Project Y spread over the Mesa. This view looks north toward the present Community Center. The Lodge is visible in the distant left, the Big House on the right.

As their first contact with that unpredictable world, Mrs. McKibbin soothed nerves, calmed fears and softened disappointments. She also supervised shipment of their belongings, issued temporary passes and arranged for their transportation up the hill to Los Alamos.

At the end of the tortuous, winding dirt road, the newcomers found a remarkable city. They found a ramshackle town of temporary buildings scattered helter-skelter over the landscape, an Army post that looked more like a frontier mining camp.

"It was difficult to locate any place on that sprawling mesa which had grown so rapidly and so haphazardly, without order or plan," wrote one early arrival.

Haste and expediency, under the urgency of war, guided every task. Equipment and supplies were trucked from the railhead at Santa Fe while temporary wooden buildings were being hastily thrown together to house them. Streets for the town and roads to remote sites were appearing daily under the blades of countless bulldozers.

The handsome log and stone Ranch School buildings, though nearly obscured by the mushrooming construction, had been converted for Project use. Fuller Lodge had become a restaurant, the classrooms had been converted to a Post Exchange and other shops, the masters' houses had become residences for top Project administrators. As the only houses in Los Alamos offering tubs instead of showers, this group of buildings quickly became known as "Bathtub Row," a name that has stuck to this day.

The hurriedly built, green Laboratory buildings sprawled along the south side of Ashley Pond. Rows of four family apartment houses spread to the west along Trinity Drive and northward; rows of barracks and dormitories bordered the apartments and overlooked the horse pastures which are now the

Top left: Sundt apartments north of Trinity Drive offered some of the most "luxurious" living on the Project. The Fermis, Bethes, Tellers, Allisons and other leading scientists lived in houses like these. Center top and bottom left: Army brought in expansible trailers and Pacific hutments such as these in a desperate effort to house the exploding population. Left: Los Alamos was constantly under construction and grew rapidly and haphazardly to complete its mission. Above: Overpasses spanned Trinity drive to connect Laboratory buildings on both sides.

Western Area. East of Ashley Pond spread the less luxurious housing including the sections known as McKeeville and Morganville.

The Army did its best to find a place for everyone. Even as the incoming population was spilling over into neighboring valley ranches, to Frijoles Lodge at Bandelier and to Santa Fe, night shift workers, maintenance crews and specialists imported from far away were pouring onto the mesa to be sandwiched in somewhere. The four-family Sundt apartments and the McKee houses were built and occupied at a frantic pace with Pacific hutments, government trailers, expansible trailers and prefabricated units following in jerry-built procession. For more than 20 years the housing never quite managed to catch up with the demand.

This unsightly assortment of accommodations ranged row on row along unpaved and nameless streets. A forest of tall metal chimneys for coal, wood and oil burning stoves and furnaces pierced the air. Soot from furnaces and dust from the streets fell in endless layers on every surface. Winter snows and summer rains left streets and yards mired in mud.

There was only one telephone line (furnished by the Forest Service) when 1943 began and only three until 1945. Dry cleaning had to be sent to Santa Fe until the establishment of a laundry and cleaning concession in the summer of 1944. The first resident dentist arrived in 1944 and a Project hospital was established the same year.

There was never enough water. Dr. Walter Cook, who organized the school system in 1943, remembers the wooden water tank that stood near Fuller Lodge. "It had a gauge on the outside that indicated the water level. It was the only way we could tell when we could take a bath."

But life in Los Alamos was not entirely primitive. A 12-grade school system with 16 teachers was established in 1943. A town council was formed the same year, its members elected by popular vote to serve as an advisory committee to the community administration. A nursery school was established for working mothers and a maid service, using Indian women from nearby pueblos, was provided on a rationing system based upon the number and ages of the woman's children and the number of hours she worked.

Top: Project housewives gather at the community laundry where washers rented for 30¢ an hour, mangles for 40¢. Center: The PX was a leisure-time gathering place. Right: Commissary offered groceries to Project residents at cost plus ten percent.

More than 30 recreational and cultural organizations were formed during the army years and in 1945 a group, including Enrico Fermi and Hans Bethe, founded a loosely knit Los Alamos University which provided lectures and published lecture notes in fields of nuclear physics and chemistry. Credits from these courses were accepted by leading universities across the country. Home grown talent provided concerts and theatrics and there were movies several times a week.

And there was the country. Los Alamos, for all its ugliness, was surrounded by some of the most spectacular scenery in America.

"Whenever things went wrong, and that was often," one resident has said, "we always had our mountains—the Jemez on one side, the Sangre de Cristos on the other."

But Los Alamos was also surrounded by a high barbed wire fence and armed guards. In what was probably the most secret project the United States has ever had, secrecy became a way of life. Laboratory members were not allowed personal contact with relatives nor permitted to travel more than 100 miles from Los Alamos. A chance encounter with a friend outside the Project had to be reported in detail to the security force.

Anonymity prevailed. Famous names were disguised and occupations were not mentioned. Enrico Fermi became "Henry Farmer", Neils Bohr became "Nicholas Baker." The word physicist was forbidden; everyone was an "engineer." Drivers licenses, auto registrations, bank accounts, income

Residents had to pass through two guard stations to get in or out of town. Later a modern stone concrete structure, now a restaurant, replaced the frame shack but access was still tightly controlled. Mounted guards patrolled the rugged boundaries of Los Alamos until the Hill became an open city in 1957.

tax returns, food and gasoline rations and insurance policies were issued to numbers. Outgoing mail was censored and long distance calls were monitored. No one was permitted to mention names or occupations of fellow residents, to give distances or names of nearby places or even to describe a beautiful view lest the location be pinpointed. Incoming mail was addressed simply to "P.O. Box 1663, Santa Fe, New Mexico," an obscurity that cloaked the existence of Los Alamos during the entire war.

Recalls one early resident, "I couldn't write a letter without seeing a censor poring over it. I couldn't go to Santa Fe without being aware of hidden eyes upon me, watching, waiting to pounce on that inevitable misstep. It wasn't a pleasant feeling."

Tight security regulations plagued scientific progress, too. The military insisted that individual scientific projects be strictly compartmentalized and not discussed so that no one could see the overall progress—or purpose—of the mission. But Director Oppenheimer, knowing that cross-fertilization of ideas among scientists is infinitely useful in solving problems, balked and as a result weekly colloquia were begun and continue in Los Alamos today. Because of such major victories as this over military rigidity, Oppenheimer is credited not only with the success of the Project but the high morale that made it possible.

The Army years at Los Alamos were a time of chaos and achievement, of unaccustomed hardships and exhausting work. But, as Oppenheimer was to report later, "Almost everyone knew that this job, if it were achieved, would be part of history. This sense of excitement, of devotion and of patriotism in the end prevailed."

Scientists like these met at weekly colloquia made possible by Oppenheimer's insistence upon a free exchange of ideas within Project. At this meeting, a nuclear-physics conference in 1946, were Oppenheimer and Richard Feynman in the second row, Norris Bradbury, John Manley, Enrico Fermi and J. M. B. Kellogg in the first.

designing the bomb

The world's first man-made atomic explosion took place only 28 months after the arrival of the first scientific contingent at Los Alamos. Few greater tributes to human ingenuity have ever been written.

The theoretical basis for nuclear weapons was already understood, in its outlines, when the Laboratory was established. Many of the engineering problems were foreseen in a general way, but much remained to be done. The following summary of weapon theory (all of it known in early 1943) will serve to suggest the enormous difficulty of the task that lay ahead.

The nucleus of an atom of uranium-235 contains 92 protons and 143 neutrons. When this nucleus absorbs an additional neutron, it becomes unstable and usually divides approximately in half. The two fragments become nuclei of two lighter elements, having a total mass somewhat *less* than the mass of the original uranium nucleus plus the additional neutron. Most of the mass difference between the original material and the products is converted into kinetic energy—rapid flight of the fragments.

The product nuclei emit several neutrons (in 1943 nobody knew exactly how many, on the average) for every U-235 nucleus split. Other U-235 nuclei may absorb these neutrons and undergo fission in turn, producing still more neutrons. Such a chain reaction will proceed very rapidly, as long as one neutron (at least) from each fission causes another fission.

Theoretically, the energy release from one kilogram (about 2.2 pounds) of U-235 would equal the energy release from the detonation of 17,000 tons of TNT.

Given these facts, the problem was to devise a bomb deriving its explosive energy from the fission of uranium-235 (or of plutonium-239, the only other fissionable material under consideration in 1943).

Neither U-235 nor Pu-239 was available in sufficient quantity to make a bomb. It was thought that these materials would become available within two years. The task of the Los Alamos staff was to design the bomb, and to devise methods of manufacturing it, in advance of the scheduled deliveries of the needed material.

A separate and remarkable story lies behind the fact that the scheduled deliveries were made on time. The story being told here will limit itself primarily to what happened at Los Alamos.

The Los Alamos task was to discover means of making the desired explosive liberation of energy take place *efficiently* and *at the right time.* A veritable mountain of difficulties stood in the way.

No one knew how much fissionable material had to be put together to support an explosive chain reaction, but it was known that the reaction could not occur if the amount were insufficient. The burning of conventional explosives is a chain reaction of a different kind; a tiny quantity of TNT burns as readily as a larger amount. Fission chains cannot occur in the same way, because the neutrons on which they depend must remain within the fuel until they encounter fissionable nuclei. If the surface area of the fuel mass is large compared to the volume (i.e., if the fuel mass is too small or too much flattened out), then the neutron escape area is too large compared to the neutron source volume, and too many neutrons will find their way out without causing fission.

By now it is possible to determine mathematically how much fuel is enough, but only when the shape, density, and purity of the fuel material are known. In 1943 additional unknowns stood in the way. The exact average number of neutrons emitted in fission had not yet been measured. Neither had the pertinent "cross sections."

The term "cross section" is an extremely useful one in the study of nuclear reactions. It is a measure of the likelihood that a certain reaction will occur, stated in terms of effective target area. Perhaps the following analogy will help to make this clear:

A popular carnival game is one in which the customer throws baseballs at ranks of woolly dolls. If we suppose that the solid portion of each doll presents a front surface of one square foot, and if we neglect the diameter of the baseball, then the effective area, ("cross section") of each doll, for the reaction we might call "direct hit," is one square foot. But if we investigate other possible reactions, we find the effective area of the same doll changing. Assume, for instance, that only one direct hit out of two causes the doll to fall down. For the "knockdown" reaction, then, the cross section of each doll is .5 square foot. If we throw ping pong balls, the "direct hit" cross section may remain one square foot, while the "knockdown" cross section becomes zero. Or, if the fringe on the doll is unusually stiff, so that a baseball passing through the fringe sometimes causes the doll to fall, then the doll's cross section for baseball knockdown may rise toward two square feet. And the knockdown cross section will be different for baseballs of different speeds. Cross

In Los Alamos by day great minds pondered the bomb problems, by night, talk turned to less secret discussions. From left to right across both pages: Enrico Fermi with L. D. P. King; Eric Jette, Charles Critchfield, J. Robert Oppenheimer; Edward Teller with Norris Bradbury; E. O. Lawrence, Fermi and I. I. Rabi.

section is the effective target area for a specific reaction or event.

If we consider a free neutron, traveling through a sphere of pure U-235 metal, we need to know how likely it is to cause fission, instead of escaping from the sphere. We need to know, in other words, not how large the U-235 nucleus actually is, but how large a target it presents statistically, for the fission reaction, to a neutron of given velocity. Fission cross sections of U-235 for neutrons of a wide range of velocities (energies) needed to be known before a bomb could be designed. Also, since the uranium would not actually be pure U-235, it was necessary to know the cross sections of various impurities, especially U-238, for neutron absorption *without* fission.

Only on the basis of careful experiments and measurements could the needed cross sections be learned. Particle accelerators (atom smashers) were used in these experiments, because they could produce, indirectly, beams of neutrons with which to bombard samples of bomb material.

The mass of a sphere of fissionable material just sufficient to sustain a chain reaction is called the "critical mass." By surrounding this material with an envelope of other material, to bounce escaping neutrons back into the active volume, it was possible to improve neutron economy and thus reduce the critical mass. Such a reflecting envelope is sometimes called a tamper.

The tamper in a weapon serves a second purpose. As the fissionable mass expands during the explosion, it quickly becomes less dense, at the same time, its surface area increases. These two effects act together to "quench" the chain reaction, since they facilitate neutron escape and reduce the likeli-

hood that a given neutron will encounter a fissionable nucleus. A massive tamper slows the expansion and allows more energy to be liberated before the reaction is quenched.

Tamper materials, especially their cross sections for capturing neutrons and for scattering neutrons back into the fissionable material, needed intensive study.

It happens that the fission cross section of U-235 is greater for slow neutrons than for fast (presumably because the slow neutron spends more time near the nucleus.) In spite of this fact, the reaction in a bomb must depend almost solely on fast neutrons. This is partly because the neutrons produced in fission are naturally fast, partly because an air-delivered bomb must be as light as possible (therefore not permitting the inclusion of moderating material to slow the neutrons), and partly because a slow-neutron reaction system would not have time to liberate a large enough fraction of the potential energy before the bomb blew itself apart.

Therefore, is was necessary to establish facts relating to the efficiency of a tamped atomic explosion produced by fast neutrons. And these facts had to be established in advance of the delivery of fissionable material for the first bomb—in advance, of course, of any atomic explosion at all.

For the sake of explosion efficiency, it was inadvisable to depend on "background" neutrons (free neutrons unavoidably present in the bomb at all times) to start the reaction. The only way to be sure the reaction would start fast, and at exactly the right moment, was to arrange an internal neutron source that would deliver millions of neutrons in a single burst at the instant of complete assembly. Devices called "initiators" had to be developed to

supply these neutrons.

As if such difficulties were not enough, a whole new supply of problems was introduced by the need to make the bomb go off at the right time and *only* at the right time.

A stick of dynamite is capable of exploding. When its cap or ignitor sets it off, it explodes. A critical mass of fissionable material is not only capable of sustaining a chain reaction; it is incapable of *not* doing so. No percussion cap is necessary. Nobody lights a fuse. Once the critical conditions exist, the reaction begins. (This is because the one free neutron needed to trigger the reaction will always be supplied within a fraction of a second by neutrons from cosmic rays, spontaneous fission, or other sources.) Therefore, the detonation of a nuclear bomb occurs whenever its core is actually and fully assembled for the first time. The final assembly must occur only at the target. To say that this introduces a problem is putting it mildly.

Furthermore, the final assembly must be accomplished rapidly. As the core passes from its subcritical, or safe, configuration to its supercritical, or explosive, configuration, it must inevitably pass through configurations that are *barely* critical. Fast assembly is necessary because there must be no time for the reaction to occur and destroy the bomb before the optimum configuration is reached.

Since no assembly method would be fast enough unless it made use of high explosives, an intensive study of the potentialities of chemical explosives for this purpose had to be made.

In principle, two general methods of assembly appeared possible. One was the so-called "gun" method, in which one subcritical mass of fissionable material would be fired as a projectile at a target consisting of another subcritical mass of fissionable material. When projectile met target, the two together would constitute a supercritical mass. (The gun, with its explosive charge and its fissionable projectile, would have to be enclosed in the bomb casing, along with the target.) The other assembly method was "implosion," in which a slightly subcritical mass of fissionable material would be surrounded by high explosives. When these explosives were detonated, they would compress the fissionable material, thereby increasing its density (decreasing the distances between target nuclei), thus rendering it supercritical.

The gun method appeared to be the easier to develop. It involved principles already well understood by ordnance experts, while the implosion method introduced entirely new principles of guiding explosive energy It was hoped that the gun method might work for both uranium and plutonium bombs. It was a somewhat slower detonation system than implosion was, but its development would require fewer technological innovations.

In 1944 came the verification of a piece of bad news rumored a little earlier: The gun method was unsuitable for plutonium bombs. The reason was that plutonium produced in nuclear reactors (such as those at Oak Ridge and Hanford) contained a significant percentage of an isotope identified as Pu-240. Plutonium of this mass number had a strong tendency toward spontaneous fission, releasing neutrons. This produced an unusually high neutron background in plutonium containing the 240 isotope. Therefore, assembly of a plutonium bomb would have to be lightning-fast to prevent premature initiation of the chain reaction. Assembly by the gun method would be too slow; in a plutonium bomb, it would have to be implosion or nothing.

The simplest way to proceed might have been to build a few experimental bombs in the early nineteen-forties and try them out. Not the least of the Laboratory's problems arose from the impossibility of doing this. By the time the precious shipments of fissionable material arrived at Los

Alamos, a workable bomb design had to be ready. Various components and sub-assemblies could be tested by themselves, but no integral test of the weapon would be possible until long after the time when such testing might have served its purpose best.

As soon as the Laboratory had its first skeleton staff and a minimum of equipment (a cyclotron loaned by Harvard University, two electrostatic accelerators from the University of Wisconsin, a Cockcroft-Walton accelerator from the University of Illinois, and much other borrowed equipment) the work began. In many ways it was a continuation of research already begun in a dozen laboratories, all over the country. But it had a focus for the first time. Los Alamos, and no other laboratory, would make the first bomb.

Research got under way on several fronts during the first half of 1943. Measurements of the "neutron number" (average number of neutrons emitted per fission) of plutonium-239 and uranium-235 were undertaken immediately, though the plutonium measurements had to be made on a sample scarcely visible to the naked eye.

Other research projects begun in the first months were these:

***Measurements of the fission spectrum (energy range) of neutrons from U-235.

***Measurements of fission cross sections of U-235 and Pu-239 for neutrons of high, low, and all intermediate energies.

***Measurements of the time (a fraction of a millionth of a second) between fission and the emission of virtually all the fission neutrons.

***Measurements of cross sections of neutron capture and neutron scattering in various possible tamper materials.

***Development of experimental techniques (including ways of producing and counting neutrons of specific energies, measuring fission in various materials, and measuring certain non-fission reactions induced by neutrons.)

***Radiochemical studies aimed toward the development of an initiator (the neutron source mentioned earlier) for the bomb.

***Research on uranium hydride, an early possibility for bomb fuel, later abandoned.

***Research on the chemistry and metallurgy of uranium and plutonium, and of possible tamper materials (including development of purification processes and analytical methods for measuring small amounts of impurities).

***Research on projectile and target materials for the gun program.

***Planning for construction of a deuterium liquefaction plant at Los Alamos, to supply liquid deuterium for experiments useful in the development of a thermonuclear bomb.

The Water Boiler reactor under construction. This reactor was constructed for use as a research tool during the development of the bomb. The world's first enriched uranium reactor, the Water Boiler is still in operation.

****An intensive ordnance program, studying the uses of high explosives for bomb assembly.

***A tremendous theoretical effort devoted to calculations of all kinds related to the physics and thermodynamics of the bomb.

At this early stage in the work of the Laboratory, it was believed that the development of the bomb would have two more-or-less distinct phases: (a) research in physics, chemistry, and metallurgy, then

Wartime photo showing one of the practical, if primitive, ways in which radioactive materials were safely handled during the early years of the bomb development.

(b) technology in engineering ordnance design. The original directive set forth a plan for putting the Laboratory on a military basis in the second phase, commissioning the scientists in military rank, and so on. As it turned out, the commissioning plan was never put into effect.

In the fall of 1943, as a result of a conference between President Roosevelt and Prime Minister Churchill, it was decided to assign about two dozen British citizens to work at Los Alamos. Among them were some of the world's most distinguished scientists.

Laboratory personnel were all civilians until the fall of 1943, when a detachment of WACs and several technicians and scientists drafted into the Army's Special Engineer Detachment (SED) joined the staff. By July, 1945, 50% of Laboratory personnel were military, mostly men of the SED. Total Laboratory personnel increased steadily from 250 in July, 1943, to 2,500 in July, 1945.

The most important single characteristic of Los Alamos Scientific Laboratory became apparent in the very first days. It has remained LASL's most important single characteristic: *The Laboratory is predominantly a scientific, not an engineering, institution.* The fact that its first mission was the creation of a practical piece of hardware would seem to contradict such a statement, but the contradiction is only an apparent one. The nature of this specific piece of hardware was such that its creation called for a massive program of scientific research.

That it also called for a massive engineering program is equally true, but not central to the character of the institution as it was in 1943 or as it has been ever since. Every development program undertaken by the Laboratory has been of such an advanced kind that the technological effort was smaller, in terms of man hours, than the scientific one. It is impossible, of course, to separate the two kinds of effort in a clear-cut way, but anyone who has worked in the intellectual climate of Los Alamos knows that "Los Alamos Engineering Laboratory" or even "Los Alamos Research and Development Laboratory" would have been a misnomer. "Scientific" is right, and the word was inserted in the earlier name, "Los Alamos Laboratory" in 1947.

The ice house, a stone building long used, before the war, for storage of ice from Ashley Pond. It later assumed historic significance as the building in which nuclear components of the first atomic bomb were assembled.

Atomic bomb research was conducted in these hurriedly constructed laboratory buildings which made up the technical area. Gamma building, below and at right above, wrapped around and obscured Ashley Pond.

preparing the materials

Preparation of the two fissionable core materials, meanwhile was being accomplished elsewhere against almost overwhelming odds.

In the case of uranium, the difficulty arose from the fact that uranium 238 and uranium 235 are almost identical substances. Each of the two kinds of atoms has 92 nuclear protons and 92 orbital electrons. Since the chemical behavior of any atom is almost entirely governed by its orbital electrons, the two kinds of uranium could not be separated by chemical processes. Some other process—a purely physical one—was required.

U-235 has 143 neutrons in each nucleus. U-238 has 146. Somehow, those three extra neutrons had to be used to make the U-238 atoms go one way and the U-235 atoms go another. A great many methods were suggested. Half a dozen or so, including a centrifuge process like the one used to separate cream from milk, were given extensive trials. Almost every idea worked, but no idea worked very well. The difference between the two isotopes was too small.

Furthermore, all of the separation methods tried were expensive. If the isotope separation program had been an industrial enterprise, aimed at making a profit, the only sensible course would have been to close up shop.

But there was a war on. Nobody knew how much effort, if any, Germany might be devoting to nuclear weapon development (actually it was very little), but one thing was almost certain: If the Germans were first to develop a nuclear weapon, Hitler would win the war. This was no time to pinch pennies.

America's decision, based partly on extremely good work by scientists in Britain, was to continue at any cost. Investigation of many ways of separating isotopes would go on, and a really vast effort would be made on the two most promising processes. One of these was gaseous diffusion separation and the other was electromagnetic separation.

Both processes are based on the difference in weight (more properly, in mass) between the two kinds of uranium nuclei.

The molecules in a gas are in constant motion. The warmer the gas, the faster its molecules move; but some move faster than others. On the average, heavier molecules are more sluggish than light ones. They move more slowly. Therefore, when a gas diffuses through a porous barrier, the lighter molecules get through a little more often (at first) than the heavier ones.

Perhaps unfortunately, uranium is not a gas. For the gaseous diffusion process, the uranium has to be combined with fluorine to produce an easily-vaporized compound called uranium hexafluoride. Uranium hexafluoride gas is extremely corrosive, tending to attack pumps, piping, barriers, and almost anything else it happens to touch.

But the gaseous diffusion method works. Passage through each barrier in a multi-stage separation plant increases (very slightly) the concentration of U-235 in some of the gas. By using thousands of stages, thousands of miles of piping, and hundreds of acres of barriers, it is possible to produce very highly enriched uranium hexafluoride. Uranium metal made from the enriched gas has a very low concentration of U-238.

A large part of the wartime project consisted of planning and building a separation plant to employ the principle just described. The plant was built in Oak Ridge, Tennessee, in the years from 1943 to 1945.

The electromagnetic separation process is quite different, but it also exploits the very slight mass differences created by the presence of those three extra neutrons in each U-238 nucleus.

Everything possessing mass has inertia. The more mass, the more inertia. It is perhaps usual to think of inertia as a reluctance to move, but inertia is a broader phenomenon than that. It is less a resistance to movement than a kind of resistance to *change*. If an object is stationary, inertia makes it reluctant to move; if it is moving, inertia makes it reluctant to stop or to change direction.

Since inertia is proportional to mass, the U-238 nucleus has a little more inertia than the U-235 nucleus. If both are traveling at the same speed, the heavier nucleus will have a slightly stronger resistance to any change in direction. Therefore, a given force tending to change the direction of motion will have a slightly greater effect on the lighter nuclei than on the heavier.

This principle is exploited in the electromagnetic separation of isotopes in the following way: First, the uranium atoms are "ionized," usually by being deprived of one orbital electron each. This leaves the atoms positively charged, so that they can be accelerated electrically and acted on magnetically. When they have been accelerated—many millions of them at a time—they are formed into a beam, all traveling in the same direction. The beam of ura-

One of eight plutonium-producing reactor facilities at Hanford works. This one operated for the first time with full loading on December 17, 1944.

nium ions is then passed through a magnetic field which has been arranged in such a way as to bend their trajectories. Under the influence of the magnetic field, the U-235 ions change direction more than the U-238 ions. The beam becomes two beams, each of which can be caught in a separate receptacle.

Though the development of the electromagnetic separation process encountered many difficulties, the method ultimately succeeded in producing important quantities of U-235. Electromagnetic separating machines called "calutrons," developed by the University of California, were installed at Oak Ridge. They were used mainly to increase the enrichment of already-enriched products of the immense gaseous diffusion plant and of a smaller thermal diffusion plant, which used uranium hexafluoride in liquid form.

By late 1944, highly enriched uranium compounds were being produced at Oak Ridge in kilogram quantities.

Meanwhile, the program to produce the previously unknown element of atomic number 94 had made great strides.

Berkeley scientists produced minute quantities of plutonium in the winter of 1940-41, by bombardment of uranium with particles from an accelerator. The new element proved to be readily fissionable, as had been predicted.

However, production in quantities of military significance could not be carried out with particle

accelerators. What was needed was a really plentiful source of free neutrons. The only sufficient source would be a nuclear fission reactor.

Fission reactors are devices in which a chain reaction is maintained under controlled conditions. No such device had been built when the Berkeley scientists produced their first plutonium. It would take two more years to achieve the first man-made fission chain reaction.

The leader in that achievement was the same Enrico Fermi who had first split the uranium nucleus. He had come to the United States and was working at the University of Chicago.

Fermi and his associates sought to demonstrate the possibility of a fission chain reaction in natural uranium—uranium containing less than one per cent U-235. Though a natural-uranium reaction would release energy at a rate unsuitable for an efficient nuclear explosion, the demonstration that such a reaction could be maintained would have great significance. Among other things, it could lead to the construction of reactors capable of producing large quantities of plutonium.

In Fermi's experiment, lumps of natural uranium metal and of natural uranium oxide were placed in a "lattice" (a system of regular spacing) within a pile of graphite blocks.

The graphite was necessary to enable the pile to sustain a chain reaction. Here is why:

When a uranium nucleus undergoes fission, neutrons come out at high velocity. In a natural uranium system, these high-speed neutrons collide with uranium nuclei of both kinds. Some of the collisions cause fission, but many others do not. Most of the neutrons become involved in a series of "elastic" (glancing or bouncing) collisions with nuclei. Such collisions do not cause fission, and each such collision robs a neutron of some of its speed.

It happens that the velocity of a neutron has a large effect on what the neutron can do to a uranium nucleus. As the velocity goes down, the neutron loses its ability to cause fission in U-238, while acquiring *even greater* ability to cause fission in U-235. At what is called "thermal" velocity (when the neutron has lost all of the initial impulse it received from the fissioning nucleus) its ability to cause fission in U-235 is very high.

Unfortunately, there is a certain intermediate velocity at which a neutron is most likely to be captured by a U-238 nucleus, without causing fission. In a chain-reacting pile using natural uranium, it is therefore desirable to prevent collisions between medium-speed neutrons and U-238 nuclei. Otherwise, so many neutrons will be captured that the chain reaction will die out. (It is exactly such captures that result in the formation of plutonium, but Fermi was not yet trying for that; his pile would require a maxium number of free neutrons, just to keep the chain reaction alive.)

By using lumps of uranium separated by blocks of graphite, it is possible to avoid many of the neutron captures that would occur in a structure of pure uranium. Neutrons produced by fissions in one lump of fuel fly out of that lump and into the graphite before they have lost enough speed to be captured readily by U-238 nuclei. In the graphite, they lose much of their velocity, because of elastic collisions with carbon nuclei. By the time the neutrons reach the next lump of fuel, they are "thermal" (slow), and are not so likely to be captured by the U-238.

Fermi's pile produced its first sustained chain reaction in December, 1942, exactly one week after the Under Secretary of War had directed that a site at Los Alamos, New Mexico, be acquired for a nuclear weapon laboratory. Fermi's success demonstrated the possibility of the sustained chain reaction and gave great encouragement to those who planned to use larger piles as neutron sources for the production of plutonium.

Construction of one such pile began in Tennessee in 1943. By November of the same year, it was in operation. Within a few months after that, it had produced several grams of plutonium.

However, much larger plutonium production reactors would be necessary for the production of enough plutonium to be used in bomb cores. In June, 1943, construction of such reactors began at Hanford, Washington, where water from the Columbia River could be used as a reactor coolant. By September, 1944, the first Hanford pile was in operation. Plutonium nitrate from Hanford would soon join the flow of fissionable material that was already moving from the uranium and plutonium production facilities in Tennessee toward the Los Alamos Laboratory.

By September, 1944, the first kilogram of highly enriched uranium (63% U-235) had been received from the separation plant at Oak Ridge. By July, 1945, 50 kilograms had been received, and the enrichment had increased to 89%.

The first small quantities of plutonium (as nitrate, not as metal) arrived at the Laboratory in October, 1943. Gram amounts were delivered early in 1944, and soon after that still larger amounts began coming in, first from Oak Ridge and later from Hanford.

Both the uranium and the plutonium needed purification (an unprecedented job) before becoming suitable for weapons use. Means of purifying these elements were developed at Los Alamos and have been constantly improved.

The problem of preparing plutonium metal of high purity was started in the Laboratory in August, 1943 at a time when no plutonium was available for research. It gradually became available in amounts varying from micrograms to grams, but in the meantime, extensive preliminary investigations of possible methods of preparation had been made using other elements as stand-ins.

By the spring of 1944, the world's first piece of plutonium metal prepared in any scale larger than a few micrograms was produced by the graphite centrifuge method which used centrifugal force to throw down molten metal into the tip of a cone during reduction. This was accomplished by placing the reaction mixture in a cone-shaped refractory liner sealed inside a steel "bomb." The bomb was then placed in a graphite centrifuge which was heated rapidly to a high temperature while rotating. As the reduction took place the metal was thrown together in the tip of the liner, producing a good yield of coherent metal.

Meantime, however, research on the stationary bomb method indicated that gravitational force alone was adequate to separate the metal from plutonium fluoride, using calcium and iodine with appropriate heating conditions. The stationary bomb method, more suited to large scale production and much less complicated than the centrifuge method, was then adopted and is still used for routine production of pure plutonium metal. The centrifuge method, however, served its purpose at a time when it was most desperately needed.

A section of the electromagnetic process equipment, used for enriching uranium at Oak Ridge, Tennessee.

Units of the electromagnetic system are used today to produce stable isotopes for peaceful purposes.

PART II

trinity

Development of the gun-type uranium weapon, which was to become "Little Boy", moved confidently ahead, but work on implosion (the method in which a subcritical mass of plutonium is compressed to supercriticality by high explosives) was slow, frustrating and often seemingly hopeless. By late 1943 it was evident that there was no alternative: the implosion device would have to be tested.

If it were not, too many questions would be left unanswered. A nuclear explosion was so entirely new, the implosion method so far removed from any existing practice, the construction of the atom bomb so entirely dependent on dead reckoning, that no one was willing to risk the first trial of such a device over enemy territory or even in demonstration for the Japanese, as had been suggested, where a failure would wipe out the crucial psychological effects of so monumental a weapon.

Furthermore, it was essential to obtain detailed and quantitative information on the various effects of the new weapon which would serve as basic technical data for tactical planning in the future. Little of this could be obtained if the explosion were first observed under combat conditions.

One important question, about which there was substantial disagreement, concerned the explosive force to be expected. Only an actual nuclear detonation could settle that question, and then only if meaningful measurements (requiring many new techniques) could be made.

Other questions concerned the performance of the implosion system inside the device; the destructive effects of heat, blast, and earth shock; radiation intensities; fallout; and general phenomena (fireball, cloud, etc.) associated with the explosion.

And so the decision was made to sacrifice what was to amount to one third of the nation's stockpile of atomic weapons and its entire supply of plutonium on a secret test on American soil.

Monument marks Ground Zero in the Jornado del Muerto where the first atomic bomb was tested. Twenty years later the land shows few scars from the momentous event.

Jumbo, the tremendous steel vessel designed to contain the explosion of the first atomic device, arrived at the siding at Pope, New Mexico, in the spring of 1945. Container was 25 feet long and weighed 214 tons.

A special 64-wheel trailer was required to carry Jumbo across the desert to Trinity site. By this time, scientists had more confidence in the implosion device and recovery plans had been abandoned.

the plans

The first formal arrangements for the test were made in March 1944 with the formation, in George Kistiakowsky's Explosives Division, of group X-2 under the leadership of Kenneth T. Bainbridge, whose duties were "to make preparations for a field test in which blast, earth shock, neutron and gamma radiation would be studied and complete photographic records made of the explosion and any atmospheric phenomena connected with the explosion."

With doubt and uncertainty hanging over the project throughout 1944 it is not surprising that one of the first and most heavily emphasized efforts in the test preparations was planning for the recovery of active material in case the nuclear explosion failed to take place. In 1944 there was barely enough plutonium available to conduct the essential experiments and the outlook for increased production was dim. It seemed absolutely essential that the active material not be wasted in an unsuccessful test.

Scientists toyed with the idea of using a water recovery method in which the bomb, surrounded by air space, would be suspended in a tank of water and fragments would be stopped by a 50 to 1 ratio of water to high explosive mass. They also investigated the possibility of detonating the bomb over a huge sand pile and putting the sand through placer operations to mine whatever plutonium might be imbedded there. Neither of these methods appeared particularly promising and the decision was made early in the game to attempt to contain the blast in a huge steel vessel.

Although the container, promptly dubbed Jumbo, became a high priority project at the outset and all test plans, until the last minute, were based on the assumption that it would be used, there is little evidence that the idea met with much enthusiasm in Los Alamos.

As early as March 10, 1944, Oppenheimer wrote to General Groves outlining the plans and possibilities for "a sphere for proof firing", pointing out that "the probability that the reaction would not shatter the container is extremely small." He promised, however, that the Laboratory would go ahead with plans and fabrication of the vessel.

But this was easier said than done, and by the following summer Jumbo had become the most agonizing of the project's endless procurement headaches.

In late March, Hans Bethe, head of the Theoretical Division, wrote in a memo to Oppenheimer that because of the numerous engineering problems, which he described in discouraging detail, "the problem of a confining sphere is at present darker than ever."

But the problem was tackled, nonetheless, by section X2-A of Bainbridge's group with R. W. Henderson and R. W. Carlson responsible for engineering, design and procurement of the vessel. In May scale model "Jumbinos" were delivered to Los Alamos where numerous tests were conducted to prove the feasibility of the design.

Feasible though the design appeared to be, there was scarcely a steel man in the country who felt he could manufacture the container. Specifications required that Jumbo must, without rupture, contain the explosion of the implosion bomb's full complement of high explosive and permit mechanical and chemical recovery of the active material. To do this required an elongated elastic vessel 25 feet long and 12 feet in diameter with 14 inch thick walls and weighing 214 tons.

Personal letters explaining the urgency of the project and the importance of the specifications went out from Oppenheimer to steel company heads, but by May 23, 1944, Oppenheimer was forced to report to his Jumbo committee that the steel companies approached had expressed strong doubts that Jumbo could be manufactured to specifications. Meanwhile, he told them, feasibility experiments would continue in the Jumbinos and the order for the final vessel would be delayed a little longer.

Eventually, the Babcock and Wilcox Corporation of Barberton, Ohio agreed to take a crack at the job and the order was placed in August, 1944. The following spring the tremendous steel bottle began its roundabout trip from Ohio on a specially built flat car, switching from one route to another wherever adequate clearance was assured. In May 1945, the jug was delivered to a siding, built for the purpose by the Manhattan District, at Pope, New Mexico, an old Santa Fe railroad station that served as a link with the Southern Pacific and the Pacific Coast in the 1890's. There it was transferred to a specially built 64-wheel trailer for the overland trip to the test site.

But it was too late. During the last months before the test, all of the elaborate recovery schemes were abandoned. By then there was greater promised production of active material, there was greater confidence in the success of the bomb and, more importantly, there was increasing protest that Jumbo would spoil nearly all the sought-after measurements which were, after all, the prime reason for conducting the test at all.

The fate of Jumbo, however, was not absolutely settled until the very last minute. On June 11, 1945, just a month before the test, Bainbridge, in a memo to Norris Bradbury, present Laboratory director and

At Trinity, Jumbo was erected on a tower 800 feet from Ground Zero. It survived the explosion unscathed.

then in charge of bomb assembly, wrote that "Jumbo is a silent partner in all our plans and is not yet dead. . . . We must continue preparations for (its) use until Oppenheimer says to forget it for the first shot."

And a silent partner it remained. Ultimately the magnificent piece of engineering was erected on a tower 800 feet from Ground Zero to stand idly by through the historic test.

Once the decision had been made, in the spring of 1944, to conduct the test, the search began for a suitable test site. Los Alamos was ruled out immediately for both space and security reasons and the search spread to eight possible areas in the western United States.

To please the scientists, security and safety people alike, the site requirements were numerous. It had to be flat to minimize extraneous effects of the blast. Weather had to be good on the average with small and infrequent amounts of haze and dust and relatively light winds for the benefit of the large amounts of optical information desired. For safety and security reasons, ranches and settlements had to be few and far away. The site had to be fairly near Los Alamos to minimize the loss of time in travel by personnel and transportation of equipment, yet far enough removed to eliminate any apparent connection between the test site and Los Alamos activities. Convenience in constructing camp facilities had to be considered. And there was the ever-present question: Could Jumbo be readily delivered there?

Throughout the spring a committee, composed of Oppenheimer, Bainbridge, Major Peer de Silva, Project intelligence officer, and Major W. A. Stevens, in charge of maintenance and construction for the implosion project, set out by plane or automobiles to investigate the site possibilities. They considered the Tularosa Basin; a desert area near Rice, California; San Nicholas Island off Southern California; the lava region south of Grants; an area southwest of Cuba, New Mexico; sand bars off the coast of South Texas; and the San Luis Valley region near the Great Sand Dunes National Monument in Colorado.

By late summer the choice was pretty well narrowed down to part of the Alamogordo Bombing Range in the bleak and barren Jornada del Muerto (Journey of Death). The area had the advantage of being already in the possession of the government and it was flat and dry although almost constantly windy. The nearest inhabitant lived 12 miles away, the nearest town, Carrizozo, was 27 miles away. It was about 200 miles from Los Alamos.

The Jornada del Muerto derives its grim name from its barren, arid landscape. Old Spanish wagon trains headed north would be left to die in the desert if they ran into trouble since they could depend on finding neither settlement nor water for 90 miles or so.

On August 14 Oppenheimer wired Groves in Washington that he thought there would be no problem in obtaining the land for their purposes but, concerned as usual about Jumbo, specified that "the northern part will be satisfactory to us provided the El Paso-Albuquerque line of the Santa Fe can carry a 200-ton load either from El Paso north or from Albuquerque south to the neighborhood of Carthage."

The final decision was made on September 7, 1944 and arrangements were made at a meeting with the commander in chief of the Second Air Force for acquisition of an 18-by-24-mile section of the northwest corner of the bombing range.

Not long afterward, when it became necessary to choose a code name for the test, it was Oppenheimer who made the selection. Many people have tried to interpret the meaning of the name but Oppenheimer has never indicated what he had in mind when he chose Trinity. In any case, it did create some confusion at first.

Bainbridge asked Oppenheimer for clarification in a memo written March 15, 1945:

"I would greatly appreciate it if the Trinity Project could be designated Project T. At present there are too many different designations. Muncy's (Business) office calls it A; Mitchell's (Procurement) office calls it Project T but ships things to S-45; and last week it was christened Project J. By actual usage, people are talking of Project T, our passes are stamped T and I would like to see the project, for simplicity, called Project T rather than Project J. I do not believe this will bring any confusion with Building T or Site T."

Nothing was simple in preparations for the test and the securing of maps of the test site was no exception. Lest Los Alamos appear involved, the job was handled by the Project's security office which managed to avoid pinpointing the area of interest by ordering, through devious channels, all geodetic survey maps for New Mexico and southern California, all coastal charts for the United States, and most of the grazing service and county maps of New Mexico. There was considerable delay while the maps were collected and sorted.

Despite the many complicated steps taken to avoid any breech of security there were a few snafus. As soon as construction began on the test site it became necessary to have radio communication within the site so that radio-equipped cars could maintain contact with the guards and with people at the various parts of the area. Later, communication would be essential between the ground and the B-29s participating in the test. A request went out to Washington for a special, exclusive wave length for each operation so that they could not be monitored.

Months went by and at last the assignments came back. But alas, the short wave system for the ground

A portion of the Alamogordo Bombing Range was chosen as the site for the Trinity test. This section of the test site was located at McDonald ranch which served as assembly headquarters for the atomic device.

was on the same wave length as a railroad freight yard in San Antonio, Texas; the ground to air system had the same frequency as the Voice of America.

"We could hear them (in San Antonio) doing their car shifting and I assume they could hear us," Bainbridge reported later. "Anyone listening to the Voice of America from 6 a.m. on could also hear our conversations with the planes."

On the basis of a thorough Laboratory survey of proposed scientific measurements to be made at the test, justification for all construction and equipment requirements was sent in a detailed memo to Groves on October 14. On November 1 Groves wired Oppenheimer his approval of the necessary construction but asked that "the attention of key scientists not be diverted to this phase unnecessarily."

He needn't have worried. By August the outlook for the implosion program had turned bleak indeed. The test preparations lost their priority and the Laboratory turned nearly all its attention toward overcoming the serious difficulties that were developing. Urgency in securing manpower for research and development on the problem was so great that all of Bainbridge's group, except for a few men in Louis Fussell's section X-2c, were forced to abandon their work on the test and concentrate on development of a workable detonating system and other top priority jobs lest there be no test at all.

Between August and February, however, Fussell's section did manage to work on such preparations as acquiring and calibrating equipment, studying expected blast patterns, locating blast and earth shock instruments, and installing cables to determine electrical and weather characteristics, in addition to the design and construction of the test site Base Camp and the design and contract for Jumbo —about all the test program could demand with the plight of implosion so desperate.

Contracts were let early in November for construction of Trinity camp, based on plans drawn up by Major Stevens in October. The camp was completed in December and a small detachment of about 12 military police took up residence to guard the buildings and shelters while additional construction continued.

As the new year arrived, the implosion work began to show more promise and the Research Division under R. R. Wilson was asked to postpone even its highest priority experiments and turn its four groups, under Wilson, John Williams, John Manley, and Emilio Segre, to developing instruments for the test.

By February the Laboratory was mobilizing. Oppenheimer had long since been committed in Washington to a test in July and the deadline was fast approaching. In a conference at Los Alamos, attended by General Groves, it was decided then and there to freeze the implosion program and concentrate on one of several methods being investigated—lens implosion with a modulated nuclear initiator. The conference then outlined a detailed schedule for implosion work in the critical months ahead:

April 2: full scale lens mold delivered and ready for full scale casting.

April 15: full scale lens shot ready for testing and the timing of multi-point electrical detonation.

March 15- April 15: detonators come into routine production.

April 15: large scale production of lenses for engineering tests begin. (Lenses direct explosive's shock waves to suitable converging point.)

April 15-May 1: full scale test by magnetic method.

April 25: hemisphere shots ready.

May 15-June 15: full scale plutonium spheres fabricated and tested for degree of criticality.

June 4: fabrication of highest quality lenses for test underway.

July 4: sphere fabrication and assembly begin. By the following month the schedule had already been shifted to establish July 4 as the actual test date and that was only the beginning of the date juggling.

Overall direction of the implosion program was assigned early in March to a committee composed of Samuel K. Allison, Robert Bacher, George Kistiakowsky, C. C. Lauritsen, Capt. William Parsons and Hartley Rowe. For its job of riding herd on the program the committee was aptly named the Cowpuncher Committee and it was the Cowpunchers who had the responsibility for the intricate job of integrating all the efforts of Project Y, the arrival of critical material from Hanford and the activities at Trinity site in order to meet the test deadline.

Trinity Base Camp was built by the Army in the winter of 1944 and was occupied by a detachment of military police from December on. By summer it was a bustling hive of activity with more than 200 scientists, soldiers and technicians.

trial run

Project Trinity, with Bainbridge as test director and William Penney and Victor Weisskopf as consultants, became an official organization and top priority project of the Laboratory in March 1945. At the same time Project Alberta, for combat delivery of the weapons, was organized under Capt. Parsons with N. F. Ramsey and Norris Bradbury as technical deputies.

Bainbridge was a Harvard physics professor with a background in electrical engineering and a three-year stint at the MIT Radiation Laboratory who had come to Los Alamos as a group leader in charge of high explosive development. As General Groves pointed out in his book, "Now It Can Be Told," Bainbridge was "quiet and competent and had the respect and liking of the more than 200 enlisted men later on duty at Alamogordo."

Bainbridge's first task was to rush his organization into preparations for a trial test—the detonation of 100 tons of conventional high explosives—which had been proposed in the winter of 1944 and scheduled for early May. Since very little was known, in 1945, about blast effects above a few tons of TNT, such a test would provide data for the calibration of instruments for blast and shock measurements and would serve as a dress rehearsal to test the operation of the organization for the final shot.

Meanwhile, a vast and complex laboratory was growing in several square miles of empty desert. There was a maze of roads to be built, hundreds of miles of wires to be strung over, on and under the ground, a complete communication system installed, buildings to be erected, supplies, equipment and personnel to be transported between Los Alamos and Trinity, all under the cloak of supreme secrecy.

The man who shouldered this monumental task was John H. Williams, leader of the Laboratory's Electrostatic Generator group, who became responsible for Trinity services as head of TR-1. As Bainbridge wrote later, "The correlation of the construction program and the proper and successful designation of construction aid was exacting work requiring 'superior judgment,' as the Army says, and long hours of hard work. This was done supremely well by Williams, to whom the Trinity project owes much for the successful completion of the operation." Bainbridge has also pointed out the invaluable assistance provided by Sgt. J. A. Jopp, who was in charge of all the wire installation and construction at the site.

Procurement of an incredible assortment of equipment ranging from Kleenex to elaborate scientific instruments was a seemingly insurmountable job handled by Robert Van Gemert, now alternate head of the Laboratory's Supply and Property Department, aided and abetted by Frank Oppenheimer who served as Bainbridge's trouble shooter.

By April the number of urgent purchase requests had increased so rapidly that it became necessary to inflate the urgency ratings that had been in use by

Hundred of miles of wires had to be strung between base camp, the control point, the instrument bunkers and Ground Zero—one of the countless jobs that kept men at Trinity working at a feverish pace throughout the spring and summer of 1945.

the Procurement Office. Until things got out of hand that spring, four ratings—X, A, B and C—had been used in order of decreasing priority. By early May, when everything seemed to warrant an X priority, it was announced that this super urgent rating would be subdivided into three others: XX, X1, and X2. XX would be used only if failure to obtain the material would produce a setback of major importance in the overall program of the Laboratory. It authorized the Procurement Office, through the Washington Liaison Office, to have recourse to the highest authority of the War Production Board and all government agencies and to use a special dispatch or cargo plane from anywhere in the United States to get delivery.

But the manufacturers were not impressed. Representatives from every armed service and government war project were pounding on their desks with equally high priorities and waiting six to 15 weeks for delivery while Trinity people were demanding three weeks delivery for the same item.

The problem was further complicated by the fact that there was no direct communication between the Project and the purchasing offices, nor could Los Alamos buyers talk directly to the scientists at the site to discuss possible substitutions or compromises on specifications.

Some items were just well-nigh impossible to get—like the seismographs that were needed to check earth shock at outlying areas around the state. The only instruments available were finally located at a firm which had already sold them to the Nazi-sympathizing Argentine government. It took an overriding directive, direct from General Grove's

office, to get the instruments shipped to Trinity instead.

Another crisis came when 10,000 feet of garden hose were lost during a shipping strike. A second order was placed but by June 29 the hose was still on the list of critical items not yet on hand. The hose was used to encase cables to sensitive instruments to protect them from the weather.

Delayed delivery on a number of urgent requests led Oppenheimer to call a meeting in May to review the procurement situation. One of the principal reasons for the delays, it turned out, was the shortage of personnel in the Los Angeles, New York and Chicago purchasing offices. Although the number of requisitions had greatly increased there had been no increase in the number of buyers since January 1944, a situation blamed on salary restrictions. As a result of the meeting salary adjustments were agreed upon and more personnel secured for all three offices. Direct communications were established between the Project and the New York and Chicago offices and Project members were asked to submit improved drawings and specifications.

But slow or not, the materials did arrive and in June the amount of goods handled by the main warehouse at Los Alamos reached its peak. During May the warehouse handled an average of 35 tons a day, 89% of which was incoming; during June the daily average rose to 54 tons of which 87% was incoming, and during the first half of July it was 40 tons a day, 80% incoming. A new shipping group was organized that spring to handle the outgoing goods, most of them bound for Trinity or Tinian Island in the Pacific.

Plenty of local procurement problems remained. First there was communication. Only five people on the project were allowed to telephone between Trinity and Los Alamos and these calls were routed to Denver, on to Albuquerque and finally to San Antonio, New Mexico. Teletype service was so bad, Van Gemert recalls, that you never knew if the test site was asking for a tube or a lube job. It soon became evident that the best way to communicate was to send notes back and forth by the truck drivers.

At least two and often as many as ten trucks left Los Alamos every evening after dark to avoid both the blistering desert heat and unnecessary notice, and arrived at the test site early the next morning. Almost always there was a stop to be made at the U.S. Engineers yard in Albuquerque to pick up items addressed to Prof. W. E. Burke of the University of New Mexico's physics department, who served as a blind to avoid a connection between the items and Los Alamos.

"We'd get things to Trinity any way we could," Van Gemert says. Some of the ways were devious. A carload of telephone poles was desperately needed at the test site and no freight train was traveling fast enough to get it there in time. After considerable urging the Santa Fe railroad consented to attach the car to the rear of the Super Chief and sped the cargo to Albuquerque. Another time, for lack of freight space, 24 rolls of recording paper were luxuriously ensconced in a Super Chief drawing room for the trip from Chicago.

To supplement the special items, the Procurement people established a complete technical stockroom at the test site early in the game and trucked the entire stock from Los Alamos. The stockroom, known officially as FUBAR (fouled up beyond all recognition), was manned by enlisted men who used their spare time to manufacture the face shields needed to protect observers from the test blast. The shields were made of aluminum sheets, mounted on a stick handle, with welders' goggles for a window.

There never seemed to be enough people to take care of all the work to be done on the test preparations and those who were available, from mess attendants to group leaders, worked at a fever pitch. A ten hour day was considered normal and it often stretched to at least 18 hours.

In the spring of 1945 a big part of the Laboratory was reorganized to take care of the test and many people found themselves involved in activities far removed from their normal duties. John Williams, the high energy physicist, took the responsibility for construction and servicing of the base camp. John Manley was wrapped up in neutron measurements as a Research Division group leader when he suddenly found himself in charge of blast measurements for the test.

"I didn't know anything about blast measurements," he recalled 20 years later. "We'd never done anything like that before."

But talent is talent wherever it is found and the displaced crews managed expertly and efficiently to bring their remarkable tasks to a successful conclusion under extreme pressure.

Throughout the spring and summer there was a constant stream of personnel traveling between Site Y and Trinity in a motley assortment of busses and cars, some of them barely able to make the long, monotonous trip.

Security precautions were rigid. In March, Dana

The flag flew at half-mast at Trinity base camp on April 12, 1945 when word came of the death of Franklin D. Roosevelt. The president's death gave Harry S. Truman the responsibility for making the crucial decision on the eventual use of the atomic bomb.

P. Mitchell, assistant director of the Laboratory, issued terse, precise travel instructions:

"The following directions are strictly confidential and this copy is to be read by no one but yourself. You are to turn this copy in to me personally on your return to the site," the memo read, and continued with specific directions and mileages for reaching the site. "Under no condition," it went on, "when you are south of Albuquerque are you to disclose that your are in any way connected with Santa Fe. If you are stopped for any reason and you have to give out information, state that you are employed by the Engineers in Albuquerque. Under no circumstances are telephone calls or stops for gasoline to be made between Albuquerque and your destination."

Travelers were then instructed to "stop for meals at Roys in Belen, which is on the left-hand side of the main road going south. If you leave the site at 7 a.m. you should make this stop around lunch time."

Even so, by midafternoon when the travelers reached the little junction town of San Antonio, most of them were hot, tired and thirsty and Jose Miera's bar and service station became a popular, if illegal, stop. Miera still remembers the unusually heavy traffic in those days. One of his customers, John Manley, remembers Miera's wall of bottles.

"He had the whole south wall of his place lined with bottles," Manley reports. "We used to worry an awful lot about that. If our big blast traveled that far, that's the wall it would hit." Luckily it didn't.

Additional regulations required that all departing groups and individuals stop at the office of the intelligence officer for an explanation of "the security objectives of Trinity." All personnel were required to sleep and eat at the camp rather than in nearby towns, and recreation trips for movies and dinners to nearby towns were prohibited to officers, enlisted men and civilians alike.

In addition, all Trinity-bound personnel were required to report their impending departure to Oppenheimer's office, to Intelligence Officer R. A. Taylor, and to Lt. Howard Bush who was trying to keep Trinity base camp running smoothly despite the constantly fluctuating population.

As Bainbridge explained in a somewhat desperate-sounding memo "to all concerned" in April 1945:

"If your schedule is planned some days ahead it will operate to the comfort of all concerned if you tell Lt. Taylor who is going down and when they are going down. Lt. Taylor will notify Lt. Bush, who can then make proper arrangements for sufficient food for the mess. Lt. Bush is issued rations three days a week—Monday, Wednesday and Friday—and he is required on a Monday trip to leave a list of his requirements to be picked up on the following Wednesday trip. This means a minimum of four days notification is necessary if there is to be sufficient food on hand so that he can avoid the present difficulties which late-comers run into of

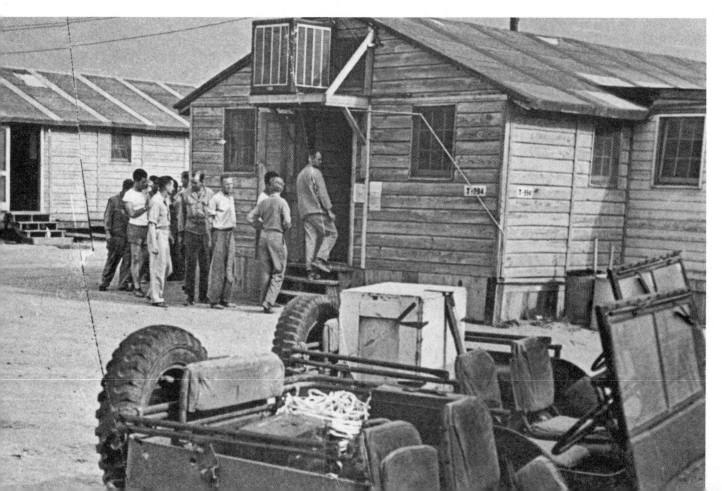

having to eat delicatessen store meat instead of the particular roast scheduled for that day. Please cooperate . . ."

There were other problems than supply and demand. Sanitary conditions in the mess hall were difficult to maintain because of the hard water. When water softening equipment was installed later it turned out that a miscalculation in water analysis resulted in a unit too small to handle the huge amounts of gypsum and lime encountered.

In the barracks, desert creatures such as scorpions had to be carefully shaken out of clothes each morning before anyone dared dress.

But despite the difficulties the camp ran well. The heat of the desert summer was relieved by swims in the cattle watering reservoirs at the old McDonald ranch. A herd of antelope disappeared from the desert range, a fact which has been attributed by the press to the ravages of the first atomic bomb. Former Trinity residents, however, admit that hunting with submachine guns was a favorite pastime and antelope steak was an almost daily part of the camp menu. So was range beef, lassoed near camp by amateur cowboys. A beer fund maintained by Laboratory people helped make up for the rules against leaving camp and there were nightly outdoor movies supplied from the Army's endless assortment of Hollywood films.

"The choice of Lt. H. C. Bush as commanding officer of the base camp," Bainbridge wrote in 1946, "was a particularly fortunate one. The wise and efficient running of the camp by Lt. Bush contributed greatly to the success of the test. It was a 'happy camp.' The excellent camp morale and military-civilian cooperation did much to ameliorate the difficulties of operation under primitive conditions."

But there were times when the excellent camp morale was put to severe test.

Back in December 1944 Bainbridge had discussed with an unidentified colleague the dangers of a possible overshoot by bombers using the Alamogordo Bombing Range for their practice runs.

"If they should go north of Area No. 3 by mistake in 1945," he wrote, "they would have to go more than 15 miles beyond the boundary in order to interfere with us. The probability that they will overshoot is likely to be very small. Let them have their fun and settle with Ickes for the White Sands National Monument."

But within a few months they were trying to settle with Bainbridge.

The chow line forms at the Base Camp mess hall. Perhaps the menu offers antelope steak.

On May 10 shortly after 1 a.m., three practice 100-pound bombs carrying five-pound black powder flash units were dropped near the Base Camp stables, setting them afire, straddling the main barracks and bringing a poker game to a sudden halt. Three days later another bomb dropped on the carpentry shop. There was no serious damage and no one was hurt.

An investigation revealed that a squadron of bombers from a base some 2500 miles away was on its final long-range practice mission before going overseas. The lead planes had hit and completely obliterated the clearly-marked bombing range targets and in the confusion the following planes assumed the well-lit camp site must be the place.

Bainbridge's suggestion that anti-aircraft guns loaded with smoke shells be used to defend the camp was rejected but no further bombing attacks were made.

On another occasion, however, a group of electricians working at a distant outpost stomped into camp headquarters, tossed a handful of spent machine gun shells on the CO's desk and resigned. It was soon discovered that gunnery crews in Alamogordo bombers were encouraged to sharpen their trigger eyes on antelope herds roaming the bombing range. For the electricians it had been too close for comfort.

The original date for the trial shot of 100 tons of TNT was May 5 but was soon shifted to May 7 to allow for installation of additional testing equipment. Many additional requests had to be refused since any further delay would have put an intolerable burden on the whole group in its attempt to meet the July test deadline.

Hundreds of crates of high explosive were brought to the site from Fort Wingate, New Mexico, and carefully stacked on the platform of a 20-foot tower. Tubes containing 1000 curies of fission products from the Hanford slug were interspersed in the pile to simulate, at a low level, the radioactive products expected from the nuclear explosion. The whole test was designed in scale for the atomic shot. The center of gravity of the high explosive was in scale with the 100 foot height for the 4,000 to 5,000 tons expected in the final test, and measurements of blast effects, earth shock, and damage to apparatus and apparatus shelters were made at scaled-in distances. Only measurements to determine "cross talk" between circuits and photographic observations were, in general, carried out at the full distance proposed for the final shot.

Then, as the last day of the European war dawned, the TNT was detonated and it was spectacular. A huge, brilliant orange ball rose into the desert sky lighting the pre-dawn darkness as far away as the Alamogordo base 60 miles southeast.

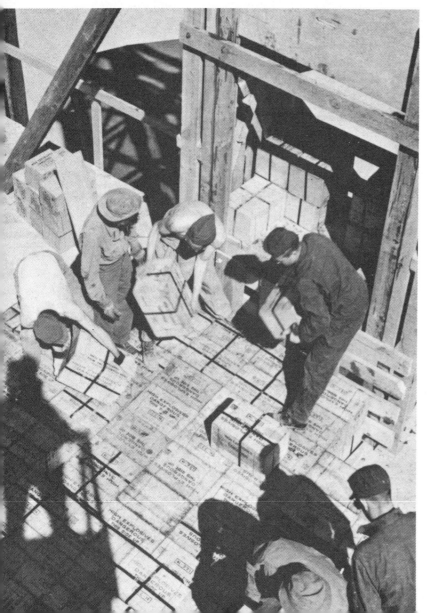

trial run   may 7, 1945

A crew prepares fission products from the Hanford slug for insertion in the high explosive for the 100-ton test. Material simulated, at a low level, the radioactive products expected from the nuclear explosion.

Completed stack of 100 tons of TNT rests on the sturdy tower, ready for the May 7 firing. Carpenters who built the tower were appalled, on returning to the site after the test, to find the structure completely obliterated.

Crates of high explosive, brought from Fort Wingate, are stacked on the 20-foot high wooden tower. The men have about 15 more rows to go before the stack will be complete.

The 100-ton explosion would have been an unforgettable sight, witnesses say, had it not been outdone so soon afterward by the nuclear explosion. Brilliant orange fireball was observed 60 miles away.

The rehearsal proved to be tremendously valuable and the high percentage of successful measurements in the final test may be attributed in large measure to the experience gained from the shot. Blast and earth shock data were valuable not only for calibrating instruments but for providing standards for the safe design of shock proof instrument shelters. Measurement of the effects from the radioactive material inserted in the stack of explosive was especially valuable in giving information on the probable amount and distribution of material which would be deposited on the ground. This information was essential for planning the recovery of equipment, the measurement of bomb efficiency, and protection of personnel for the final shot.

The test also gave the men, accustomed to well-equipped laboratories, a familiarity with the tribulations of field work, and perhaps most importantly, showed up some defects in the test operations while there was still time to correct them.

Immediately after the test Bainbridge asked for lists of complaints about the operations from the various group leaders involved and on May 12, while the experience was still fresh in everyone's minds, held a gripe session to discuss suggestions for improvements.

Far and away the biggest complaint was transportation. Nearly everyone felt there were not enough roads between Ground Zero and the various shelters and the roads that did exist were in intolerable condition. The dust and ruts were hard on both personnel and instruments and the two-wheel drive GI sedans were constantly getting bogged down in a foot or so of soft, loose sand. They also asked for more vehicles and more repair men who could service the cars at night to avoid delays and keep up with the demand.

To overcome poor communications throughout the test site, new phone lines, public address systems to shelters and short wave radios in automobiles were requested as well as a building in which to hold meetings.

Everybody complained of lack of help to get things done on time and asked in particular for more help on procurement, shipping and stock management and a direct teletype to the Los Alamos Procurement Office.

The group felt the operation was severely handicapped by the interminable delays caused by rigid restrictions on the movement of personnel in and out of the various areas just before the test. They asked for and got free access to all parts of the test area during the last few hours before the shot.

Only one man complained about camp food.

As a result of the meeting, 20 miles of black top road had to be laid, new structures built and a new communication system installed. After the test, too, a major effort had to be devoted to the final timing devices. Each experiment required different time schedules, some having to start ahead of Zero, others requiring a warning pulse only 1000th of a second ahead of the detonation. The circuits were the responsibility of Joseph McKibben and the electronic timing device was developed by Ernest Titterton of Australia. In addition to these chores there were the weak spots pointed out in the trial test to be overcome. And there was precious little time to do it.

As early as April hopes of meeting the original Independence Day deadline had begun to dim. Delays in the delivery of full scale lens molds and the consequent delay in the development and production of full scale lenses, as well as the tight schedule in production of active material made it necessary to reconsider the date, and on June 9 the Cowpuncher Committee agree that July 13 was the earliest possible date and July 23 was probable.

In a memo to all his group leaders on June 19, Oppenheimer explained that although July 4 was accepted as a target date in March, "none of us felt that date could be met." He then announced the Cowpuncher decision and explained, "In reaching this conclusion we are influenced by the fact that we are under great pressure, both internally and externally, to carry out the test and that it undoubtedly will be carried out before all the experiments, tests and improvements that should reasonably be made, can be made."

And so the pressure mounted, security tightened and preparation went on with increasing speed and intensity.

At Trinity the work goes on. Above: Julian Mack and B. C. Benjamin pause for a quick breakfast. Opposite, top: Berlyn Brixner handles a drill in preparation for camera installations at N 10,000. Middle: Benjamin and George Econnomu prepare charges for shock velocity determinations. Bottom: Darol Froman cuts pipe.

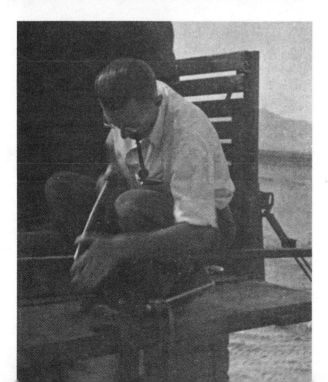

countdown

The air hung heavy over the Hill that summer. Rains failed to come and precipitation was half the normal amount. Temperatures rose to average four degrees above normal. Water became scarce and fires threatened, adding to the irritations and frustrations.

Dorothy McKibbin, who ran the Santa Fe liaison office for the Los Alamos project, could discern the tightening of tensions on the Hill, but because of rigid security, she had only her intuition to tell her what was happening. As many as 70 people checked into her office every day and one day she counted 100 phone calls. "The voices on the telephone showed strain and tautness, and I sensed we were about to reach some kind of climax in the project," she recalls.

In the Laboratory, one or two hour meetings, attended by consultants, group and section leaders involved in the Trinity Project, were being held every Monday for consideration of new experiments, correlation of the work, detailed scheduling and progress reports.

One of the most important corrective measures resulting from the 100-ton test had been the setting of a date after which further apparatus, particularly electrical equipment, could not be introduced into the experimental area. The deadline would allow plenty of time for dry runs and would reduce the risk of last minute damage to electrical connections. In view of this, proposed experiments were described in writing in great detail and submitted to a special examining committee. If approved they were then submitted to the Monday meetings where they were considered with respect to the test programming as a whole before being accepted. "Any new experiment had to be awfully good to be included after the deadline." Bainbridge reports.

For about a month before the test, John Williams held nightly meetings at Trinity to hear reports on field construction progress and to plan the assignment of men for the following day. Construction help was assigned on the basis of needs and priority of experiments which had been accepted for the test.

Meanwhile, J. M. Hubbard, who had joined the Trinity Project early in April, as meteorology supervisor, had undertaken the job of determining the best test date from a weather point of view.

Weather was a vital factor. Clear weather was best suited to observation planes in the air and visual and photographic measurements on the ground. Rain before or during the test could damage electrical circuits both for firing the gadget and

Guard stations were set up—some in tents, some in trucks—to check the goings and comings of personnel throughout the test site. Movement was restricted; various areas required different badge designations.

operating the instruments. Only six months before the test, according to General Groves, Joseph Hirschfelder, a Los Alamos physicist, had first brought up the possibility that fallout might be a real problem. For this reason it was considered essential that wind direction be such that the radioactive cloud would not pass over inhabited areas that might have to be evacuated, and there should be no rain immediately after the shot which would bring concentrated amounts of fallout down on a small area.

Using reports from each group on the particular weather conditions or surveys they would find most useful and coordinating them with complete worldwide weather information, Hubbard ultimately pinpointed July 18-19 or 20-21 as the ideal date with July 12-14 as second choice. July 16 was mentioned only as a possibility.

However, on June 30 a review of all schedules was made at a Cowpuncher meeting for which all division leaders had submitted the earliest possible date their work could be ready. On the basis of these estimates, July 16 was established as the final date.

From the beginning, estimates of the success of the gadget had been conservative. Although safety provisions were made for yields up to 20,000 tons, test plans were based on yields of 100 to 10,000 tons. By as late as July 10 the most probable yield was set at only 4,000 tons.

Scientists not directly involved in the test established a pool on the yield and the trend was definitely toward the lower numbers, except for Edward Teller's choice of around 45,000 tons. Oppenheimer himself reputedly picked 200 tons and then bet $10 against Kistiakowsky's salary that the gadget wouldn't work at all. (I. I. Rabi, project consultant, won the pool with a guess of 18,000 tons, a number he picked only because all the low numbers had been taken by the time he entered the contest.)

It was not just the yield that was in doubt. Even as the scientists went about the last few weeks of preparations, the nagging uncertainty persisted about whether the bomb would work at all. This air of doubt is depicted in a gloomy parody said to have circulated around the Laboratory in 1945:

"From this crude lab that spawned a dud
Their necks to Truman's axe uncurled
Lo, the embattled savants stood
And fired the flop heard round the world."

Then, as if things weren't looking dismal enough, a meeting of Trinity people held just before the test heard Hans Bethe describe in depressing detail all that was known about the bomb, and all that wasn't. Physicist Frederick Reines remembers the utter dejection he felt after hearing the report. "It seemed as though we didn't know anything," he said.

It was only natural, Bethe wrote later, that the scientists would feel some doubts about whether the bomb would really work. They were plagued by so many questions: Had everything been done right? Was even the principle right? Was there any slip in a minor point which had been overlooked? They would never be sure until July 16.

By the first week in July, plans were essentially complete and the hectic two weeks that remained were devoted to receiving and installing equipment, completing construction, conducting the necessary tests and dry runs and, finally, assembling the device.

The plans, as described in the official AEC history, "The New World," were these:

"Working in shelters at three stations 10,000 yards south, west and north of the firing point, teams of scientists would undertake to observe and measure the sequence of events. The first task was to determine the character of the implosion. Kenneth Greisen and Ernest Titterton would determine the interval between the firing of the first and last detonators. This would reveal the degree of simultaneity achieved. Darol Froman and Robert R. Wilson would calculate the time interval between the action of the detonators and the reception of the first gamma rays coming from the nuclear reaction. From this value they hoped to draw conclusions as to the behavior of the implosion. With Bruno Rossi's assistance, Wilson would also gauge the rate at which fissions occurred.

"Implosion studies were only a start. The second objective was to determine how well the bomb accomplished its main objective—the release of nuclear energy. Emilio Segre would check the intensity of the gamma rays emitted by the fission products, while Hugh T. Richards would investigate the delayed neutrons. Herbert L. Anderson would undertake a radiochemical analysis of soil in the neighborhood of the explosion to determine the ratio of fission products to unconverted plutonium. No one of these methods was certain to provide accurate results, but the interpretation of the combined data might be very important.

"The third great job at Trinity was damage measurements. John H. Manley would supervise a series of ingenious arrangements to record blast pressure. Others would register earth shock while William G. Penney would observe the effect of radiant heating in igniting structural materials. In addition to these specific research targets, it was important to study the more general phenomena.

Station South 10,000 served as the main control point for the Trinity test. Robert Oppenheimer, Bainbridge and General Farrell were among those who watched the explosion from this bunker.

This was the responsibility of Julian E. Mack. His group would use photographic and spectrographic observations to record the behavior of the ball of fire and its aftereffects." Some cameras would take color motion pictures, some would take black and white at ordinary speeds and others would be used at exceedingly high speeds, up to 8000 frames per second, in order to catch the very beginning of the blast wave in the air. There also would be several spectrographs to observe the color and spectrum of the light emitted by the ball of fire in the center of the blast.

Observation planes, one of them carrying Capt. Parsons, head of the overseas delivery project, would fly out of Albuquerque making passes over the test site to simulate the dropping of a bomb. They would also drop parachute-suspended pressure gauges near Ground Zero. One of the main reasons for the planes would be to enable Parsons to report later on the relative visual intensity of the explosion of the test bomb and that of the bomb to be dropped on Japan.

Plans also were made to cover the legal and safety aspects of the test.

To protect men and instruments, the observation shelters would be located 10,000 yards from Ground Zero and built of wood with walls reinforced with concrete and buried under huge layers of earth. Each shelter was to be under the supervision of a scientist until the shot was fired at which time a medical doctor would assume leadership. The medics were familiar with radiation and radiation instruments and would be responsible for efficient

McDonald ranch, used for final assembly of the active material, still stands at Trinity.

evacuation of the shelters on designated escape routes in case of emergency. Vehicles would be standing by ready to leave on a moments notice, manned by drivers familiar with the desert roads at night. Commanding the shelters would be R. R. Wilson and Dr. Henry Barnett at N 10,000, John Manley and Dr. Jim Nolan at W 10,000 and Frank Oppenheimer and Dr. Louis Hemplemann at S 10,000.

A contingent of 160 enlisted men under the command of Major T. O. Palmer were to be stationed north of the test area with enough vehicles to evacuate ranches and towns if it became necessary and at least 20 men with Military Intelligence were located in neighboring towns and cities up to 100 miles away serving a dual purpose by carrying recording barographs in order to get permanent records of the blast and earth shock at remote points for legal purposes.

On July 5, just six days after enough plutonium had been received, Oppenheimer wired Project consultants Arthur H. Compton in Chicago and E. O. Lawrence in Berkeley:

"Anytime after the 15th would be a good time for our fishing trip. Because we are not certain of the weather we may be delayed several days. As we do not have enough sleeping bags to go around, we ask you please not to bring any one with you."

There wasn't much sleeping being done anywhere at Trinity those last frantic days. There were about 250 men from Los Alamos at the test site doing last minute technical work and many more were in Los Alamos contributing to the theoretical and experimental studies and in the construction of equipment. And all of them were working against time.

"The Los Alamos staff was a dedicated group," John Williams is quoted as saying some years later.

"It was not uncommon to have a 24 hour work day at the end."

On July 1 the final schedule was broadcast at Trinity and circulated around the camp two days later. Rehearsals would be held July 11, 12, 13 and 14. Originally scheduled to be held in the afternoon, the times were changed after the first dry run when daily afternoon thunderstorms began to interfere with the flight of the observation planes and to produce electrical interference and pick up on the lines.

Meanwhile, Norris Bradbury, group leader for bomb assembly, had issued his countdown. Beginning on July 7 in Los Alamos the high explosive components were put through a number of tests to study methods of loading and the effects of transportation and a dry run on the assembly. On July 10 the crew began the tedious round-the-clock preparations of the components for delivery to Trinity, using night shifts to get the job done. Thursday, July 12, assembly began at V site and by late that night they were ready to "seal up all holes in the case; wrap with scotch tape (time not available for strippable plastic), and start loading on truck."

At 1 a.m. on Friday, July 13, the pre-assembled high explosive components started for Trinity in a truck convoyed by Army Intelligence cars in front and behind with George Kistiakowsky accompanying the precious cargo in the forward car.

The two hemispheres of plutonium made the trip to Trinity from Los Alamos on July 11, accompanied by a Lt. Richardson and several soldiers in a convoyed sedan and delivered to Bainbridge at the tower. A receipt for the plutonium was requested.

"I was very busy and we were fighting against time," Bainbridge recalled recently. "I thought 'What kind of foolishness is this,' and directed the men to the assembly site at McDonald ranch."

Bainbridge remembers that Richardson and his crew seemed awfully eager to get rid of their strange cargo even though they weren't supposed to know the real significance of it.

Eventually the receipt was signed at the ranch by Brig. Gen. T. F. Farrell, Groves' deputy, and handed to Louis Slotin who was working on nuclear assembly. The acceptance of the receipt signaled the formal transfer of the precious Pu-239 from the Los Alamos scientists to the Army for use in a test explosion.

Nuclear tests and the assembly of the active components were completed at the ranch and shortly after noon on Friday the 13th final assembly of the bomb began in a canvas tent at the base of the tower.

Bradbury's detailed step-by-step instructions for the assembly process, which was interrupted at frequent intervals for "inspection by generally interested personnel," show the careful, gingerly fashion in which the crew approached its history-making job.

"Pick up GENTLY with hook."

"Plug hole is covered with a CLEAN cloth."

"Place hypodermic needle IN RIGHT PLACE. Check this carefully."

"Insert HE—to be done as slowly as the G (Gadget) engineers wish. . . . Be sure shoe horn is on hand."

"Sphere will be left overnight, cap up, in a small dish pan."

By late afternoon the active material and the high explosive came together for the first time.

Neither Bradbury nor Raemer Schreiber, a member of the pit assembly crew, remembers any particular feeling of tension or apprehension during the operation although, Bradbury said, "There is always a certain amount of concern when you are working with high explosives."

"We were given plenty of time for the assembly of active material," Schreiber remembers. "By then it was pretty much a routine operation. It was simply a matter of working very slowly and carefully, checking and re-checking everything as we went along."

The assembly departed from the routine only once, when the crew made the startling discovery that the two principal parts of the gadget, carefully designed and precision machined, no longer fit together. Marshall Holloway, in charge of pit assembly, came to the rescue and in only a couple of minutes had the problem solved.

Active material for the Trinity device is moved from the sedan that brought it to McDonald ranch.

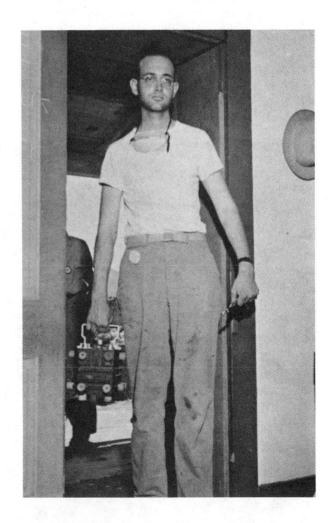

Initiators for the gadget are delivered to the McDonald ranch assembly room in a shock-proof case.

The plutonium component, which had generated a considerable amount of its own heat during the trip from Los Alamos, had expanded. The other section of the assembly had remained cold. The heat exchange resulting when the hot material was left in contact with the cold for only a minute or two soon had the two pieces slipping perfectly together.

Early the next morning the tent was removed and the assembled gadget was raised to the top of the 100-foot tower where it rested in a specially constructed sheet steel house. But it was still without detonators.

"Detonators were very fragile things in those days," Bradbury explained. "We didn't want to haul that gadget around with the detonators already in it. We might have dropped it."

So it was up to the detonator crew, headed by Kenneth Greisen, to climb the tower and make the final installations and inspections and to return every six hours to withdraw the manganese wire whose induced radioactivity was a measure of neutron background. The necessary cables were connected to a dummy unit which would permit tests to continue while the bomb was armed.

Late that night the job was essentially complete. The gadget was left in the care of an armed guard and the scientists and technicians were left with only the final routine preparations and last-minute adjustments on their equipment.

All planes at the Alamogordo base were grounded until further notice and arrangements had been made with the Civil Aeronautics Authority, the Air Corps and Navy to insure that the entire area would be barred to all aircraft during the last important hours.

According to General Groves, it was quite upsetting to the base, for it was there that B-29 crews received their final training before leaving for the Pacific and every unit commander wanted his crew to have as many hours in the air as possible. All they knew was that their training schedules were being upset for some unexplained reason. Many men, Groves continued, were already on the landing field when the explosion occurred and not long after several thousand men were preparing for take-offs.

Meanwhile, the high-ranking observers began to assemble. On Sunday afternoon General Groves, who had been touring Manhattan District installations on the West Coast in order to be nearby in case the test hour was advanced, arrived at Trinity with Vannevar Bush and James B. Conant, members of the MED's policy committee. A busload of consultants from Project Y left Los Alamos for the desert and automobiles were dispatched to Santa Fe to pick up Charles A. Thomas, MED's coordinator for chemical research, and to Albuquerque for Ernest O. Lawrence, Sir James Chadwick and William L. Laurence of the New York *Times,* the one newsman assigned by the Manhattan District to document the development of the bomb.

At the test site, after months of hectic activity, things became more relaxed as the final items on Bradbury's hot run countdown indicate:

"Sunday, 15 July, all day: Look for rabbit's feet and four-leafed clovers. Should we have the chaplain

down there? Period for inspection available from 0900-1000.

Monday, 16 July, 0400: BANG!"

But it wasn't quite as simple as that. By Sunday evening the skies had darkened, thunder rolled in the surrounding mountains and lightning cracked through the overcast. It began to rain. Now that the test was ready, at long last, could it actually go?

Shortly before 11 p.m. Sunday night the arming party, consisting of Bainbridge, Kistiakowsky, Joe McKibben, two Army weathermen, Lt. Bush and a guard, assembled at the base camp for the final trip to the tower.

McKibben, who had the very important and punishing job of supplying the timing and remote operating signals, was dead tired. "He had had a more trying time for two weeks than most of us," Bainbridge recalled. "Any one of 50 people with special test equipment who needed timing and activating signals over their control wires had been asking McKibben and his group for rehearsals at all hours of the day and night for two weeks with very large amounts of business the week prior to July 16."

But tired or not, McKibben had with him a two-page check list of 47 jobs to be done before Zero hour. His preliminary jobs were finished by 11 and he was urged to get some sleep. "I remember he looked absolutely white with fatigue," Bainbridge said, "and we wanted him alert and ready at test time."

Donald Hornig came out, went to the top of the tower to switch the detonating circuit from the dummy practice circuit to the real gadget and then returned to S 10,000 where he would be responsible for the "stop" switch. If anything went wrong while the automatic devices were operating seconds before the detonation, he would pull the switch and prevent the explosion.

Kistiakowsky climbed about 30 feet up the tower to adjust a light at the radioed request of a camera-man and then returned to the car to sleep. Periodically Lt. Bush or the guard turned their flashlights on the tower to make certain there was no one trying to interfere with the cables. Hubbard and his assistants continued with their weather measurements while Bainbridge kept in touch with John Williams on the land telephone at S 10,000.

"It was raining so hard," McKibben remembers, "I dreamed Kisti was turning a hose on me." There was lightning, too, but not dangerously close to the tower. The rain continued. Back at the control dug-

On July 14 the tent was removed and the device, completely assembled except for the detonators, was raised to the top of the 100-foot tower.

out Oppenheimer and General Groves consulted through the night.

"Every five or ten minutes Oppenheimer and I would go outside and discuss the weather," Groves writes. "I was shielding him from the excitement swirling about us so that he could consider the situation as calmly as possible."

Fortunately, Groves continues, "although there was an air of excitement at the dugout, there was a minimum of conflicting advice and opinions because everyone there had something to do, checking and re-checking the equipment under their control."

At 1 a.m. Groves urged the director to get some sleep. Groves himself joined Bush and Conant in a nearby tent for a quick nap without much luck. "The tent was badly set up," Groves recalls, "and the canvas slapped constantly in the high wind."

By 2 a.m. the weather began to look better and it was decided that the shot probably could be fired that morning, but instead of the planned hour of 4 a.m. it was postponed until 5:30. The waiting and checking continued.

The rain stopped at 4:00 a.m. At 4:45 a.m. the crucial weather report came: "Winds aloft very light, variable to 40,000 surface calm. Inversion about 17,000 ft. Humidity 12,000 to 18,000 above 80%. Conditions holding for next two hours. Sky now broken becoming scattered." The wind directions and velocities at all levels to 30,000 feet looked good from a safety standpoint. Bainbridge and Hubbard consulted with Oppenheimer and General Farrell through Williams on the telephone. One dissenting vote could have called off the test. The decision was made. The shot would go at 5:30.

The arming party went into action. Bainbridge, McKibben and Kistiakowsky drove with Lt. Bush to the west 900 yard point where, according to Mc-Kibben's check list, he "opened all customer circuits." Back at the tower connections were checked, switches were thrown and arming, power, firing and informer leads were connected. Bainbridge kept in touch with Williams by phone, reporting each step before it was taken.

"In case anything went sour," Bainbridge explained, "the S 10,000 group would know what had messed it up and the same mistake could be avoided in the future."

The lights were switched on at the tower to direct the B-29s and the arming party headed for the control point at S 10,000, driving, they all insist, at the reasonable rate of about 25 miles an hour.

Arriving at S 10,000 about 5 a.m. Bainbridge broadcast the weather conditions so that leaders at the observation points would have the latest information and know what to worry about in the way of fallout.

Ready for the countdown, the first atomic device waits in its steel shelter at the top of the tower. Opposite page: The formation of the fireball during the first four seconds after detonation.

Then from Kirtland Air Force Base came word from Captain Parsons. Weather was bad at Albuquerque and the base commander did not want the planes to take off. But the decision was already made.

Later the planes did take off but because of overcast only fleeting glimpses of the ground could be seen and Parsons was barely able to keep the plane oriented. Unable to drop their gauges with any degree of accuracy the airborne group became merely observers.

Just after 5 Bainbridge used his special key to unlock the lock that protected the switches from tampering while the arming party was at the tower. At 5:10 a.m. Sam Allison began the countdown.

All through the night the spectators had been gathering to await the most spectacular dawn the world had ever seen.

They waited on high ground outside the control bunker. They waited at the observation posts at West and North 10,000. They waited in arroyos and in surrounding hills. A group of guards waited in slit trenches in Mockingbird Gap between Oscuro and Little Burro Peaks.

All had been instructed to lie face down on the ground with their feet toward the blast, to close their eyes and cover them as the countdown approached zero. As soon as they became aware of the flash they could turn over and watch through the darkened glass that had been supplied.

On Compagna Hill, 20 miles northwest of Ground Zero, a large contingent of scientists waited along with Laurence of the *Times*. They shivered in the cold and listened to instructions read by flashlight by David Dow, in charge of that observation post. They ate a picnic breakfast. Edward Teller warned about sunburn and somebody passed around some sunburn lotion in the pitch darkness.

Fred Reines, a former Los Alamos physicist, waited with Greisen and I. I. Rabi, a project consultant, and heard the "Voice of America" burst forth on the short wave radio with "Star Spangled Banner" as if anticipating a momentous event.

Al and Elizabeth Graves, a husband and wife scientific team, waited in a dingy Carrizozo motel with their recording instruments. Others, mostly military men, waited at spots as far away as 200 miles, their instruments ready to record the phenomena.

In San Antonio, Restaurant Proprietor Jose Miera was awakened by the soldiers stationed at his place with seismographs. "If you come out in front of your store now, you'll see something the world has never seen before," they told him.

Just south of San Antonio, a group of hardy Los Alamos souls, who had climbed into the saddle of Chupadero Peak the day before, waited drowsily in their sleeping bags.

In Los Alamos, most people slept but some knew and went out to watch from the porches of their Sundt apartments. Others drove into the mountains for a better view. Mr. and Mrs. Darol Froman and a group of friends waited in their car, gave up and were heading back down the mountain when 5:30 came.

A group of wives, whose husbands had been off in the desert for endless weeks, waited in the chill air of Sawyer's Hill. Months later one of them described the agonizing hours.

"Four o'clock. Nothing was happening. Perhaps something was amiss down there in the desert where one's husband stood with other men to mid-wife the birth of the monster. Four fifteen and nothing yet. Maybe it had failed. At least, then, the husbands were safe. . . . Four thirty. The gray dawn rising in the east, and still no sign that the labor and struggle of the past three years had meant anything at all. . . . It hardly seemed worthwhile to stand there, scanning the sky, cold and so afraid."

Elsewhere the world slept or fought its war and President Truman waited at Potsdam.

Back at Trinity, over the intercoms, the FM radios, the public address system, Sam Allison's voice went on, counting first at five-minute intervals then in interminable seconds.

"Aren't you nervous?" Rabi asked Greisen as they lay face down on the ground.

"Nope," replied Greisen.

"As we approached the final minute," Groves wrote, "the quiet grew more intense. I was on the ground (at Base Camp) between Bush and Conant. As I lay there in the final seconds, I thought only of what I would do if the countdown got to zero and nothing happened."

Conant said he never knew seconds could be so long.

At the control point, General Farrell wrote later, "The scene inside the shelter was dramatic beyond words. . . . It can be safely said that most everyone present was praying. Oppenheimer grew tenser as the seconds ticked off. He scarcely breathed. He held on to a post to steady himself."

The countdown went on. At minus 45 seconds Joe McKibben threw the switch that started the precise automatic timer. Now it was out of man's control, except for Hornig who watched at his post at the stop switch.

Minus 30 seconds, and Williams and Bainbridge joined the others outside the control dugout.

Minus 10 seconds. Cool-headed Greisen changed his mind. "Now I'm scared," he suddenly blurted to Rabi.

Then, as the world teetered on the brink of a new age, Sam Allison's voice cried, "Now!"

the new world

At that instant—5:29:45 a.m. Mountain War Time on July 16, 1945—came an incredible burst of light, bathing the surrounding mountains in an unearthly brilliance. Then came the shock wave that knocked over two men at S 10,000, then the thunderous roar. A vast multi-colored cloud surged and billowed upward. The steel tower that held the bomb vanished, the tower that held Jumbo, 800 feet away, lay crumpled and broken on the ground.

Wrote Enrico Fermi shortly after the test:

"My first impression of the explosion was the very intense flash of light, and a sensation of heat on the parts of my body that were exposed. Although I did not look directly towards the object, I had the impression that suddenly the countryside became brighter than in full daylight. I subsequently looked in the direction of the explosion through the dark glass and could see something that looked like a conglomeration of flames that promptly started rising. After a few seconds the rising flames lost their brightness and appeared as a huge pillar of smoke with an expanded head like a gigantic mushroom that rose rapidly beyond the clouds, probably to a height of the order of 30,000 feet. After reaching full height, the smoke stayed stationary for a while before the wind started dispersing it."

Fermi then went on to explain the simple experiment he took time to conduct that helped considerably in making the first early estimates of the bomb's success.

"About 40 seconds after the explosion the air blast reached me. I tried to estimate its strength by dropping from about six feet small pieces of paper before, during and after the passage of the blast wave. Since, at the time, there was no wind, I could observe very distinctly and actually measure the displacement of the pieces of paper that were in the process of falling while the blast was passing. The shift was about two and a half meters, which at the time, I estimated to correspond to the blast that would be produced by ten thousand tons of TNT."

Hans Bethe wrote that "it looked like a giant magnesium flare which kept on for what seemed a whole minute but was actually one or two seconds. The white ball grew and after a few seconds became clouded with dust whipped up by the explosion from the ground and rose and left behind a black trail of dust particles. The rise, though it seemed slow, took place at a velocity of 120 meters per second. After more than half a minute the flame died down and the ball, which had been a brilliant white became a dull purple. It continued to rise and spread at the same time, and finally broke through and rose above the clouds which were 15,000 feet above the ground. It could be distinguished from the clouds by its color and could be followed to a height of 40,000 feet above the ground."

Joe McKibben recalls that "we had a lot of flood lights on for taking movies of the control panel. When the bomb went off, the lights were drowned out by the big light coming in through the open door in the back."

"After I threw my last switch I ran out to take a look and realized the shock wave hadn't arrived yet. I ducked behind an earth mound. Even then I had the impression that this thing had gone really big. It was just terrific."

"The shot was truly awe-inspiring," Bradbury has said. "Most experiences in life can be comprehended by prior experiences but the atom bomb did not fit into any preconception possessed by anybody. The most startling feature was the intense light."

Bainbridge has said that the light was the one place where theoretical calculations had been off by a big factor. "Much more light was produced than had been anticipated."

A military man is reported to have exclaimed, "The long-hairs have let it get away from them!"

While scientists were able to describe the technical aspects of the explosion, for others it was more difficult.

"Words are inadequate tools for acquainting those not present with the physical, mental and psychological effects. It had to be witnessed to be realized," wrote General Farrell two days later. Nonetheless, many tried to describe the historic moment.

Farrell himself wrote:

"The effects could well be called unprecedented, magnificent, beautiful, stupendous, and terrifying. No man-made phenomenon of such tremendous power had ever occurred before. The lighting effects beggared description. The whole country was lighted by a searing light with the intensity many times that of the midday sun. It was golden, purple, violet, gray and blue. It lighted every peak, crevasse and ridge of the nearby mountain range with a clarity and beauty that cannot be described but must be seen to be imagined. Seconds after the explosion came, first, the air blast pressing hard against the people, to be followed almost immediately by the strong, sustained awesome roar which warned of doomsday and made us feel we puny things were blasphemous to dare tamper with the forces heretofore reserved for the Almighty."

William L. Laurence, whose sole job was to write down the moment for history, wrote:

"It was like the grand finale of a mighty symphony of the elements, fascinating and terrifying, uplifting

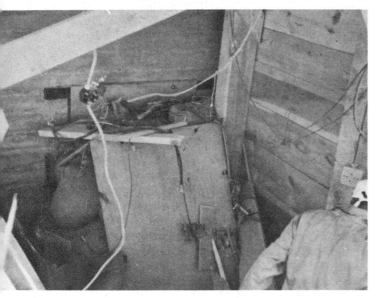

Damage to the instrument shelter at North 1000 is shown in the two top photos. At the bottom, Jumbo stands unscathed, its tower crumpled around it.

and crushing, ominous, devastating, full of great promise and great foreboding."

Another time he said, "On that moment hung eternity. Time stood still. Space contracted to a pinpoint. It was as though the earth had opened and the skies split. One felt as though he had been privileged to witness the Birth of the World—to be present at the moment of Creation when the Lord said: Let there be light."

Oppenheimer, on the other hand, has said he was reminded of the ancient Hindu quotation:

"I am become Death, the destroyer of worlds."

At the time, however, probably few actually thought of the consequences of their work, beyond ending the war. Bradbury said recently, "For that first 15 seconds the sight was so incredible that the spectators could only gape at it in dumb amazement. I don't believe at that moment anyone said to himself, 'What have we done to civilization?' Feelings of conscience may have come later."

Bainbridge reports that his reactions were mixed. "When the bomb first went off I had the same feelings that anyone else would have who had worked for months to prepare this test, a feeling of exhilaration that the thing had actually worked. This was followed by another quick reaction, a sort of feeling of relief that I would not have to go to the bomb and find out why the thing didn't work."

But later he told Oppenheimer, "Now we're all sons of bitches."

Ernest O. Lawrence is quoted as saying that from his vantage point on Compagna Hill, "the grand, indeed almost cataclysmic proportion of the explosion produced a kind of solemnity in everyone's behavior immediately afterwards. There was a restrained applause, but more a hushed murmuring bordering on reverence as the event was commented upon."

At the control point, Farrell wrote, "The tension in the room let up and all started congratulating each other. All the pent-up emotions were released in those few minutes and all seemed to sense immediately that the explosion had far exceeded the most optimistic expectations and wildest hopes of the scientists."

Kistiakowsky, who had bet a month's salary against $10 that the gadget would work, put his arms around the director's shoulder and said, "Oppie, you owe me $10."

Elsewhere the momentous event had not gone unnoticed. The flash of light was seen in Albuquerque, Santa Fe, Silver City, Gallup and El Paso. Windows rattled in Silver City and Gallup. So intense was the light that a blind girl riding in an automobile near Albuquerque asked, "What was that?"

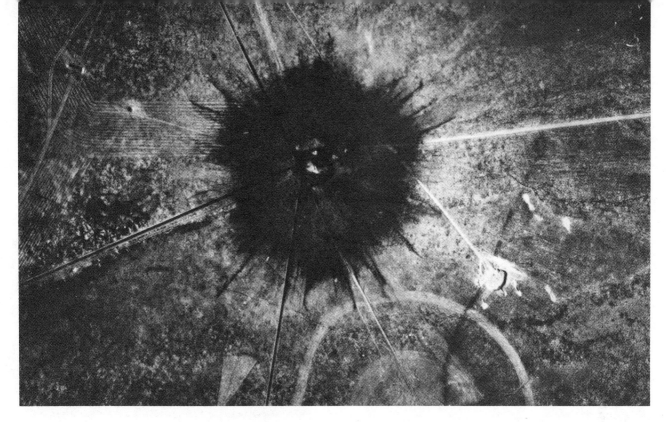

Crater and heat effects scar the desert at Ground Zero.

A rancher between Alamogordo and the test site was awakened suddenly. "I thought a plane had crashed in the yard. It was like somebody turned on a light bulb right in my face."

Another man, 30 miles away in Carrizozo, recalls, "It sure rocked the ground. You'd have thought it went off right in your back yard."

A sleepless patient in the Los Alamos hospital reported seeing a strange light. The wife, waiting on Sawyer's Hill behind Los Alamos, saw it too, and wrote later:

"Then it came. The blinding light like no other light one had ever seen. The trees, illuminated, leaping out. The mountains flashing into life. Later, the long slow rumble. Something had happened, all right, for good or ill."

At the test site, as the spectators watched the huge cloud billow into the sky, the medical officers took over leadership of the three observation points, watching their counters and maintaining contact with Paul Aebersold's crew of monitors patrolling the roads within the test site. An Entry Permission Group, consisting of Bainbridge, Dr. Hemplemann and Aebersold kept track of the reports and made decisions on movement of personnel around the site.

At first there was no sign of danger. Then suddenly, the instruments at N 10,000 began clicking rapidly showing that radioactivity was on the rise. Dr. Henry Barnett, in charge of the shelter, gave the order to evacuate and soon the trucks and cars were roaring past W 10,000 and on to Base Camp. It later proved to be a false alarm. Film badges worn by the personnel at the observation point indicated that no radioactivity had reached the shelter.

Before long those without further duties were permitted to return to Base Camp and those with instruments in the forward areas moved in to pick them up.

As the sun came up, air currents were created which swept radioactivity trapped in the inversion layer into the valley. Geiger counters at S 10,000 began to go wild. The few men remaining there put on masks and watched anxiously as the radioactive air quickly moved away before the danger level was reached. Around 9:30 a.m. Bainbridge radioed the men in the slit trench at Mockingbird Gap to return to Base Camp.

Shortly afterward a lead-lined tank, driven by Sgt. Bill Smith and carrying Herbert Anderson and Enrico Fermi, moved in to Ground Zero to recover equipment and to study debris in hope of getting information on long range detection of atomic explosions. The tank was equipped with a trap door through which earth samples could be safely picked up in the crater.

Fermi later reported to his wife that he found "a depressed area 400 yards in radius glazed with green, glass-like substance where the sand had melted and solidified again."

Meanwhile, General Groves, who had planned to wait at Base Camp until all danger of fallout was passed, hoped to make good use of the hours by discussing with Los Alamos people a number of problems connected with the next job on the agenda, the bombing of Japan.

"These plans were utterly impracticable," he wrote later, "for no one who had witnessed the test was in a frame of mind to discuss anything. The success was simply too great. It was not only that we had achieved success with the bomb; but that everyone—scientists, military officers and engineers—realized we had been personal participants and eye-witnesses to a major milestone in the world's history."

But Groves had other problems to keep him busy anyway.

The explosion had generated considerable excitement around the state and as far away as El Paso. At Associated Press in Albuquerque, the queries coming in were becoming more difficult to handle. Intelligence Officer Lt. Phil Belcher, now the Laboratory's Documents Division leader, was stationed at Albuquerque to keep any alarming dispatches about the explosion from going out. About 11 a.m. the AP man told Belcher he could no longer hold back the story. If nothing is put out now by the Army, he told him, AP's own stories would have to go on the wire.

The Army was prepared for this kind of determination. Weeks before a special press release had been prepared and sent to the Alamogordo Bombing Range with Lt. W. A. Parish from Groves' office. With it, Parish also carried a letter to the commanding officer, Col. William Eareckson, instructing him to follow Lt. Parish's instructions, no questions asked.

About 11 Parish was instructed to make his release:

Alamogordo, July 16—The Commanding Officer of the Alamogordo Army Air Base made the following statement today:

"Several inquiries have been received concerning a heavy explosion which occurred on the Alamogordo Air Base reservation this morning.

"A remotely located ammunition magazine containing a considerable amount of high explosives and pyrotechnics exploded.

"There was no loss of life or injury to anyone, and the property damage outside of the explosives magazine itself was negligible.

"Weather conditions affecting the content of gas shells exploded by the blast may make it desirable for the Army to evacuate temporarily a few civilians from their homes."

The news ran in New Mexico papers and spread up and down the West Coast by radio. It didn't fool everyone. Some days later, Groves reports, he was dismayed when a scientist from the Hanford project said to him: "By the way, General, everybody at DuPont sends their congratulations."

"What for?" the general asked innocently.

"This is the first time we've ever heard of the

This special lead-lined tank was used by Enrico Fermi and Herbert Anderson for obtaining soil samples from the crater shortly after the test.

Recovery team and radiation monitors assemble for action a few hours after the test.

Army's storing high explosives, pyrotechnics and chemicals in one magazine," he replied.

Colonel Eareckson has since been nominated by sympathetic historians as one of the unsung heroes of World War II. Not only was he forced to take the blame for this gross mishandling of explosives, but he had to take his orders that day from a mere lieutenant.

By late afternoon it was clear there would be no difficulty with fallout. Bainbridge finally left the control center about 3 p.m. to return to the Base Camp for food and rest. General Groves, Conant and Bush left for Albuquerque to begin the trip back to Washington.

Groves' secretary, Mrs. Nora O'Leary, who had been standing by in Washington since early morning for word of the test, received a coded message from her boss and at 7:30 p.m. sent the following message to Secretary of War Stimson at Potsdam:

"Operated on this morning. Diagnosis not yet complete but results seem satisfactory and already exceed expectations. Local press release necessary as interest extends a great distance. Dr. Groves pleased. He returns tomorrow. I will keep you posted."

Although it would be weeks before the measurement could be correlated and interpreted it was immediately apparent that the implosion weapon was a technical success. The fire ball, Fermi's calculations with bits of paper and other data available immediately indicated the yield had been greater than the most optimistic predictions. It was therefore possible for Groves to follow up his first message to Potsdam with another optimistic one the next day:

"Doctor has just returned most enthusiastic and confident that the little boy is as husky as his big brother. The light in his eyes discernible from here to Highhold and I could hear his screams from here to my farm."

The message was clear. The power to crush Japan had taken on a new dimension. The device had worked beyond expectations, its flash seen for 250 miles, its thunder heard for 50, and Groves was sure the plutonium bomb was as potent as the uranium gun.

Through the day of July 16, cars of weary, excited men headed back toward Los Alamos. There was still a great deal of work to be done and for those who were going overseas, the test had simply been a rehearsal.

A new Fat Man was scheduled to be delivered August 6.

When they stopped for meals in Belen the men talked of inconsequential things and listened to mystified citizens discussing the strange sort of thunder they had heard that morning and the way "the sun came up and went right back down again."

Occupants of one car did not recognize the occupants of the other. Security was as tight as ever. It was not until they reached the guarded gates of Los Alamos that the flood of talk burst loose.

Mrs. Fermi recalls the men returning late that evening. "They looked dried out, shrunken. They had baked in the roasting heat of the southern desert and they were dead tired. Enrico was so sleepy he went right to bed without a word. On the following morning all he had to say to the family was that for the first time in his life on coming back from Trinity he had felt it was not safe for him to drive. I heard no more about Trinity."

But during the day, rumors of the brilliant light so many had watched for and seen spread through the town. Although few people knew officially what had happened, most were able to sense or guess that the project to which each had contributed his part had been accomplished.

When he returned to the Hill that night, Fred Reines found the town jumping. One of the janitors Reines knew spotted the returning scientist, grinned proudly and said, "We did it, didn't we?"

"We sure did," Reines told him.

At Potsdam, where President Truman and Prime Minister Churchill were waiting to meet with Stalin to discuss a demand for unconditional surrender from the Japanese, the news of the successful test of the Fat Man that morning had a profound effect. Confidence in the test results and the reassurance that the first bomb could be ready for delivery on July 31 froze the previously tentative decision that the time had come to issue the surrender ultimatum. The atomic bomb had made invasion unnecessary and could provide the Japanese with an honorable excuse to surrender. The war could end quickly. There was no longer any need for help from Russia. Churchill and Truman approached the talks in extreme confidence.

There never had been much doubt that the gun-type uranium weapon would work. By July 14, two days before the implosion weapon was tested, the major portion of the U-235 component began its journey overseas from Los Alamos. A few hours before dawn on July 16, just as observers in the Jornada del Muerto were witnessing the incredible birth of the atomic age, the uranium bomb was hoisted aboard the cruiser Indianapolis at San Francisco.

On July 26, the Indianapolis arrived at Tinian and two nights later transport planes arrived with the last necessary bit of U-235 and the uranium device was ready.

The world's second man-made nuclear explosion occurred over Hiroshima, Japan, on August 6, three weeks after the Trinity test. On August 9, the third such explosion devastated the city of Nagasaki. Japan gave up the struggle five days later, and surrender ceremonies were held September 2.

they built the bomb

Kenneth Bainbridge
Test Director

These men directed the atomic bomb project at Los Alamos. Most were division leaders, some played other key roles. None of them was alone. There were dozens more brilliant young scientists who made significant contributions. There were countless technicians, administrative people, soldiers and WACs without whom the work could not have been done. Not the least were the wives to whom, John Williams once said, should go much of the credit. "They lived in uncertainty and sometimes fear during those trying years. They never knew what their husbands were doing and they never asked."

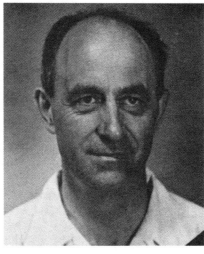

Enrico Fermi
Theory

Hans Bethe
Theory

John Williams
Deputy Test Director

George Kistiakowsky
Explosives

Robert Bacher
Weapons Physics

Maj. Gen. Leslie R. Groves
Director
Manhattan Engineer District

J. Robert Oppenheimer
Director

Victor Weisskopf
Theory

John von Neumann
Theory

Robert Wilson
Physics Research

Cyril Smith
Metallurgy

Eric Jette
Plutonium Metallurgy

William Parsons
Ordnance

SANTA FE NEW MEXICAN

The Oldest Newspaper in the Southwest, Founded in 1849

Vol. 96, No. 213 | MEMBER AUDIT BUREAU OF CIRCULATIONS | SANTA FE, NEW MEXICO, MONDAY, AUGUST 6, 1945 | ASSOCIATED PRESS UNITED PRESS | Price 5c

Los Alamos Secret Disclosed by Truman

ATOMIC BOMBS DROP ON JAPAN

By WILL HARRISON

Last week's "Big I" handout from the Governor's office was today still reverberating in educational and legislative circles.

Governor Dempsey was quoted in the news handout as saying:

"During the 1943 Legislature I sponsored a bill which transferred all of the mineral leasing act funds, except that portion used for free textbooks and the Bureau of Mines, to the school equalization fund."

The act, in two years, has produced $1,165,173 for the school equalization fund.

Comes today a letter from Sen. J. H. Mullis of Roswell:

"Before the 1943 Legislature I conferred with J. D. Shinkle, superintendent of the Roswell schools, Col. E. L. Lusk of the New Mexico Military Institute, and Clarence E. Hinkle, president of the Roswell board of education, regarding legislation which would increase the teachers' salaries. We decided on three bills:

"1.—To transfer to the school fund, to be used to increase the teachers' salaries, the balance of the Mineral Leasing Act fund, mentioned by Governor Dempsey;

"2.—Reducing from 5 per cent to 3 per cent the amount allowed the Bureau of Revenue for collecting the sales tax;

"3.—Limiting the Commissioner of Public Lands to $100,000 per year.

"I had these bills prepared before the Legislature convened and Governor Dempsey had nothing to do with the preparation of these bills. It is my recollection that Governor Dempsey was opposed to the mineral funds bill because it took that amount from the general fund.

"I introduced the bills and with the help of the New Mexico Educational Association secured the passage of the first but the Governor had the other two killed."

As noted in this space Saturday, the teachers act which the Governor said "I sponsored" was permitted to pass only after the school lobby consented to support a Dempsey measure permitting the transfer of certain surplus administrative funds to the state general fund.

And after the "I sponsored bill" became law the administration even then tried to grab part of the mineral leasing money for other than school support. Nov. 20, 1943, state records show, Governor Dempsey's State Board of Finance ordered $85,612.16 of mineral leasing money transferred to the general fund. Educational groups put up a fight and on Nov. 29, 1943, the amount was returned on the authority of an Attorney General's opinion

Although the schools received during the past two years $1,165,173 as a result of the "I sponsored bill" a complete and truthful statement would show that funds almost equalling that amount were taken from the schools by Dempsey sponsored bills in the same Legislature that enacted the mineral leasing funds law.

The transfer law, for which Dempsey traded with the school lobby, in the past two years has taken $357,593.64 for the general fund that would otherwise have gone to schools. ($163,106.71 from surplus in emergency school tax administrative fund in 1945, and $95,000 in 1944; $69,486.93 from surplus in income tax administration fund in 1945, and $30,000 in 1944.)

A total of $514,000 from the Casual Indebtedness fund was transferred to the general fund when no deficit existed. This money, under administrations prior to Dempsey, would have been transferred to the schools as witnessed June 30, 1942, when Gov. John Miles transferred to the schools $145,761.24 of casual deficit funds which were not needed to meet actual deficits.

The transfers under Dempsey of casual deficit money to the state general fund were $262,000 in 1944 and $252,000 in 1945.

Net Gain $283,580

The sum of these losses to school funds is $871,593.64, leaving a net gain through the mineral easing funds law of $283,580.

And that gain may be credited to Sen. J. H. Mullis of Roswell and the New Mexico Educational Association who first fought the administration and then traded out with the Governor for the increased revenue.

$700 STOLEN

Mrs. Ida M. Glynn, living in one of La Posada's cabins, reported to city police that $700 was stolen from a purse which she had hidden under a pillow in one of her rooms. The money included a $500 bill, police said.

Deadliest Weapons in World's History Made In Santa Fe Vicinity

Santa Fe learned officially today of a city of 6,000 in its own front yard.

The reverberating announcement of the Los Alamos bomb, with 2,000 times the power of the great Grand-Slammers dropped on Germany, also lifted the secret of the community on the Pajarito Plateau, whose presence Santa Fe has ignored, except in whispers, for more than two years.

Decision to locate the Atomic Bomb Project Laboratory on mesa an hour's drive from Santa Fe, meant that it was necessary for the Army Engineers to construct an entirely new town to house the workers and their families. Primary reason for selection of the isolated site was security.

Ranch School Site

When the Army took over the property early in 1943 there were a few buildings which had been occupied by the Los Alamos Ranch School. New buildings began going up at once. Today there are 37 in the main technical area and about 200 others on the property used for the project itself. Three hundred buildings containing 620 family units, also were constructed, as well as military barracks, hospital buildings and structures for administrative offices.

Dr. J. R. Oppenheimer, one of the foremost physicists in the country and director of the laboratory, came to the site during early stages of construction. Other scientists and technical workers followed soon after.

Scientific groups which had been working on the project elsewhere in the country moved in rapidly, bringing their equipment with them. The Harvard cyclotron was in operation six weeks after it had reached the site.

Tortuous Route

Nearest railroad facilities are at Albuquerque and Santa Fe. This made it necessary to truck everything from those cities, at least. The road from Santa Fe is a tortuous one, and in the beginning, the last 18 miles were not paved. This was bad enough for passenger cars, and presented a particularly tough problem in hauling heavy loads.

Today the community has more than 6,000 residents. Slightly less than two-thirds are civilian men, women and children and the remainder military personnel. The post commandant is Col. Gerald R. Tyler.

First need of arriving personnel in mess halls, or in a large cafeteria, was housing. Various types were constructed, to meet different needs. There are three-room prefabricated, individual houses; three-room apartments, eight to a building, and four- and five-room apartments, four in a two-story unit. There are some hutments, Quonset-type huts and government and personally-owned trailers.

Bachelor Dorms

Dormitories have been constructed for unmarried personnel, or persons who do not have their families with them. Rents, for family groups, are based on earnings. Apartments are unfurnished and family groups ordinarily bring their furniture with them, although some items of government furniture have been available.

Housewives shop for food for daily meals at an army commissary where ration points are as important as elsewhere. A "trading post" offers items needed in everyday life and there are the usual post exchange stores.

Personnel living in dormitories eat There is also a dining room with waitress service.

City Dads, Too

A "town council" of eight elected members serves in an advisory capacity, meeting with representatives of the project and of the commanding officer. There is a school board, appointed by Colonel Tyler and Doctor Oppenheimer, which oversees operation of an accredited elementary school and high school. There

(Continued on Back Page)

REVOLUTIONARY

News of the development at Las Alamos of an atomic bomb immediately raised conjecture regarding the potential industrial uses of the energy.

The power of the atomic force harnessed by scientists in the secret projects is almost beyond comprehension—one bomb packing the wallop of the bomb loads of 2,000 Superforts. Talk was at once heard of the possibility of the newly controlled energy replacing coal, electricity, gasoline, water as a source of power.

That the study of the subject will continue was assured by the appointment by the Secretary of War of a committee to carry on investigation of atomic energy.

Spokesmen for the Las Alamos project said they had not been informed if this meant post-war continuation of the mountain project.

TERRITORIAL CHANGES OF WORLD WAR II—Black areas on map are those parts of Germany which the Big Three proposes will come under Polish rule. Shaded area is territory which Russia has taken control over since the start of hostilities on the continent. Northern East Prussia, proposed as Russian by the Big Three, is the newest addition to Soviet territory. There still remains some question as to final disposition of the port of Stettin. Note the large section of Baltic coastline of the proposed new Poland.

4 More Nippon Cities Now Smoldering Ruins

By The Associated Press

American airmen said they turned four more forewarned Japanese cities to ashes today as 750 Superforts and Mustang fighters reportedly swept the enemy's sacred islands with fire bombs, rockets and parachuted mines.

B-29 crewmen returning to their Marianas Island bases told of setting fires visible for 150 miles at sea. Some ran into intense antiaircraft fire and strong interception including rocket planes as they raided cities Tokyo described as "defenseless".

Waves of B-29s from the Marianas Islands and Mustang fighters from Iwo Jima struck as American commanders announced 70 Nipponese ships and small craft and 61 locomotives were destroyed or damaged in previous aerial blows, reaching over 4,500 miles from Paramushiro to Singapore.

Terror-ridden China carried the brunt of ground actions. Elsewhere land armies hunted for Japanese generals in the northern Philippines, drove toward trapping the largest Japanese force remaining in New Guinea and counted 13,000 Nipponese dead in recent fighting in monsoon-swept south Burma.

Superforts warned 12 more cities Sunday morning they were on their fire list. A formation of 580 followed up today by lighting towering fires in four of the 31 forewarned cities.

Today's targets include Nishinomiya, noted in prewar days for producing Japan's best sake, favorite alcoholic beverage of Nippon. The other industrial targets were Maebishi, 60 miles from Tokyo, saga on northern Honshu Island, and Imbari, on the southern island of Honshu. One B-29 unit hammered the Ube coal liquefaction plant with high explosives.

Japanese also reported Mustangs from Iwo raked the capital with rockets, bombs and machinegun bullets in daylight for the third time in four days.

For consolation, Japanese propagandists reported: Americans "lead a starvation life;" Nipponese raiders caught U. S. planes lined up wing to wing on two Okinawa air fields; a U. S. submarine was sunk off the coast of Japan; Nipponese subs sank two Allied vessels in the central Pacific.

Chinese reports told of new terror in China. Once-beautiful Kweilin, former southeast China air base city, was left thoroughly sacked. Fifty-thousand Chinese were killed or missing from Kanhsien in east central China. A thousand civilians were reported killed by forced poisonous injections at Ichang, enemy-held central China river port.

Americans and Filipinos eliminated an ambushing Japanese company and beat back two desperate counterattacks on northern Luzon island, running last week's toll in the Philippines to 4,740 Japanese killed and 444 taken prisoner. U. S. losses for the week were 27 killed, ti wounded.

Maj. Gen. William Gill offered a 45-day furlough to any member of the 32d Division who captures an enemy general alive. Chief prize is Gen. Tomoyuki Yamashita, onetime "Tiger of Malaya" variously reported cornered, killed or flown from northern Luzon mountains.

Hi Johnson Dies at 79

WASHINGTON, Aug. 6 (AP)—Sen. Hiram W. Johnson of California, militant opponent of the League of Nations and the San Francisco Charter for a United Nations organization, died today.

The veteran Republican senator succumbed at Naval Hospital, where he had been confined for 2½ weeks. His physician, Capt. Robert E. Duncan, USH, said he died from a thrombosis of a cerebral artery.

The 79-year-old Californian died at 6:45 a. m., after having been in ill health for some time.

His political activities extended over a third of a century covering some of the most stirring events in the nations history.

A striking figure in the Senate since first elected to Congress in 1916, he played a leading part in defeating President Wilson's League of Nations Covenant and later in opposing United States' adherence to the World Court.

His wife, whom he referred to as "the boss," was with him at the time of his death.

Senator McKellar (D.-Tenn.), President of the Senate, today will appoint a committee to attend the funeral of the silver-haired veteran.

'Utter Destruction,' Promised in Potsdam Ultimatum, Unleashed; Power Equals 2,000 Superforts

WASHINGTON, Aug. 6 (AP)—The U. S. Army Air Force has released on the Japanese an atomic bomb containing more power than 20,000 tons of TNT.

It produces more than 2,000 times the blast of the largest bomb ever used before.

The announcement of the development was made in a statement by President Truman released by the White House today.

The bomb was dropped 16 hours ago on Hiroshima, an important Japanese army base.

The President said that the bomb has "added a new and revolutionary increase in destruction" on the Japanese.

Mr. Truman added:

"It is an atomic bomb. It is a harnessing of the basic power of the universe. The force from which the sun draws its power has been loosed against those who brought war to the Far East."

The base that was hit is a major quartermaster depot and has large ordnance, machine tool and aircraft plants.

The raid on Hiroshima, located on Honshu Island on the shores of the Inland sea, had not been disclosed previously although the 20th Air Force on Guam announced that 580 Superforts raided four Japanese cities at about the same time.

The city of 318,000 also contains a principal port.

2 Billion Gamble

The President disclosed that the Germans "worked feverishly" in search of a way to use atomic energy in their war effort but failed. Meantime American and British scientists studied the problem and developed two principal plants and some lesser factories for the production of atomic power.

The President disclosed that more than 65,000 persons now are working in great secrecy in these plants, adding:

"We have spent $2,000,000,000 on the greatest scientific gamble in history — and won."

"We are now prepared to obliterate more rapidly and completely every productive enterprise the Japanese have above ground in any city. We shall completely destroy Japan's power to make war."

The President noted that the Big Three ultimatum issued July 26 at Potsdam was intended "to spare the Japanese people from utter destruction" and the Japanese leaders rejected it. The atomic bomb now is the answer to that rejection and the President said "they may expect a rain of ruin from the air, the like of which has never been seen on this earth."

Process Secret

Mr. Truman forecast that sea and land forces will follow up this air attack in such numbers and power as the Japanese never have witnessed.

The President said that this discovery may open the war for an entirely new concept of force and power. The actual harnessing of atomic energy may in the future supply the power that now comes from coal, oil and the great dams, he said.

"It has never been the habit of the scientists of this country or the policy of this government to withhold from the world scientific knowledge," Mr. Truman said. "Normally therefore everything about the work with atomic energy would be made public." That will have to wait, however, he said, until the war emergency is over.

MADE IN SANTA FE

WASHINGTON, Aug. 6 (AP)—The atomic bomb disclosed by President Truman today was developed at factories in Tennessee, Washington and New Mexico.

Mr. Truman said that from 65,000 to 125,000 workers were employed on the project at Oak Ridge near Knoxville, Tenn., at Richland near Pasco, Wash., and at an unnamed installation near Santa Fe, New Mexico.

He said the work was so secret that most of the employes did not know the character of it.

WILL SHORTEN WAR

WASHINGTON, Aug. 6 (AP) — Secretary timson predicted today that the atomic bomb will "prove a tremendous aid" in shortening the war with Japan.

The war secretary made his statement as the Army reported that an "impenetrable cloud of dust and smoke" cloaked Hiroshima after it was hit by the new weapon from the air.

An accurate assessment of the damage inflicted by the bomb is not yet available, however, the War Department said. As soon as details of its effectiveness are learned, the department added, they will be released.

PUNCH CATASTROPHIC

WASHINGTON, Aug. 6 (AP) — The atomic bomb announced by President Truman today packs a punch equivalent to that normally delivered by 2,000 B-29s.

The President said the missile has an explosive force equal to 20,000 tons—40,000,000 pounds—of TNT. Assuming a B-29 carries a bomb load of 10 tons of TNT, four 500-plane raids by the world's biggest bombers would be necessary to equal in destructive power the exploding fury of one atomic bomb.

The atomic bomb dwarfs by 2,000 times the blast power of the British "grand-slam" bomb, which weighed approximately 11 tons.

LONDON, Aug. 6 (AP)—Germany possessed some atomic power secrets, Winston Churchill said tonight, but "by God's mercy, British and American science outpaced all German efforts."

May Be Tool To End Wars; New Era Seen

Mankind's successful transition to a new age, the Atomic Age, was ushered in July 16, 1945, before the eyes of a tense group of renowned scientists and military men gathered in the desertlands of New Mexico to witness the first hand results of their $2,000,000,000 effort. Here in a remote section of the Alamogordo Air Base 120 miles southeast of Albuquerque the first man-made atomic explosion, the outstanding achievement of nuclear science, was achieved at 5:30 a. m. of that day.

Mounted on a steel tower, a revolutionary weapon destined to change war as it has been known, or which may even be the instrumentality to end all wars, was set off with an impact which signalized man's entrance into a new physical world. Success was greater than the most ambitious estimates. A small amount of matter, the product of a chain of huge specially constructed industrial plants, was made to release the energy of the universe locked up within the atom from the beginning of time.

Credit J. R. Oppenheimer

This phase of the Atomic Bomb Project, which is headed by Maj. Gen. Leslie R. Groves, was under the direction of Dr. J. R. Oppenheimer, theoretical physicist of the University of California. He is to be credited with achieving the implementation of atomic energy for military purposes.

Tension before the actual detonation was at a tremendous pitch. Failure was an ever-present possibility. Too great a success, envisioned by some of those present, might have meant an uncontrollable, unusable weapon.

Final assembly of the atomic bomb began on the night of July 12 in an old ranch house. As various component assembles arrived from distant points, tension among the scientists rose to an increasing pitch. Coolest of all was the man charged with the actual assembly of the vital core, Dr. R. F. Bacher, in normal times a professor at Cornell University.

Lightning Threatens

On Saturday, July 14, the unit which was to determine the success or failure of the entire project was elevated to the top of the steel tower.

The ominous weather which had dogged the assembly of the bomb had a very sobering effect on the assembled experts whose work was accomplished amid lightning flashes and peals of thunder.

Nearest observation point was set up 10,000 yards south of the tower where in a timber and earth shelter the controls for the tests were located. At a point 17,000 yards from the tower at a point which would give the best observation the key figures in the atomic bomb project took their posts. These included General Groves, Dr. Vannevar Bush, head of the Office of Scientific Research and Development, and Dr. James B. Conant, president of Harvard University.

Lie Face Down

Actual detonation was in charge of Dr. K. T. Bainbridge of Massachusetts Institute of Technology. He and Lieutenant Bush, in charge of the Military Police Detachment, were the last men to inspect the tower with its cosmic bomb.

At the Base Camp, all present were ordered to lie on the ground, face downward, heads away from the blast direction.

Tension reached a tremendous pitch in the control room as the deadline approached. The several observation points in the area were tied in to the control room by radio and with 20 minutes to go, Dr. S. K. Allison of Chicago University took

(Continued on Back Page)

Tomato Juice Off Rationing

WASHINGTON, Aug. 6 (AP)—Grocers scratched point values today from canned tomato juice, mixed vegetable juice and grapefruit-orange juice blends.

OPA's action in making those products ration-free yesterday followed a recommendation from Secretary of Agriculture Anderson based on lowered military demands.

Anderson also announced that civilian store shelves will get 10,000,000 more cases of canned vegetables from this year's pack than had been expected.

Despite the 10 per cent increase, however, the Agriculture Department said the total still will be less than last year's.

SENTENCED

Pat Chavez, 333 Urioste Street, faced a 100-day jail sentence and $100 fine today on conviction before Peace Justice A. E. P. Robinson of assault and battery on a woman taxi driver. The court reported the case Saturday as involving a Pat Lopez and called attention today to the correct name of the defendant.

Now They Can Be Told Aloud, Those Stoories of 'the Hill'

By WILLIAM McNULTY

The secret of Los Alamos is out and The New Mexican staff and other newspapermen through New Mexico can heave a sigh—sigh, nothing; it's more of a groan—of relief.

President Truman's revelation today that it was an atomic bomb THEY were working on on The Hill ended what was probably the strictest censorship ever imposed upon the press of this state. There was practically no limit to the lengths that the guards went to and the situation at times became fantastically involved including the famed "Battle of the MPs."

Notwithstanding the censorship, the news of Los Alamos had scarcely raced about the Plaza this morning when the membership of the "I-Knew-It-All-Along" club began growing by leaps and bounds. As a matter of record, the most recent rumor, No. 6,892—straight from the horse's mouth last week—was that Alamos was working lickety-split, night and day, in the production of windshield wipers for submarines.

The taboo on the mention of Los Alamos was final, complete and until today, irrevocable and not susceptible to any exceptions whatsoever.

A whole social world existed in nowhere in which people were married and babies were born nowhere. People died in a vacuum, autos and trucks crashed in a vacuum and the MPs baseball team materialized out of a vacuum, trained in a vacuum and after their games at Fort Marcy Park, returned to the vacuum. Even the graduates of Los Alamos Ranch School, the institution which preceded Uncle Sam's Atomic Bomb Project Laboratory, ceased to be graduates of Los Alamos; they bounded direct from Public School No. 7 clear into the classrooms of Harvard and Yale.

And on days when the Alamos experimenters threw their atomic bombs about a little too vigorously and the windows of Santa Fe rattled ominously, this paper's phones would ring but the whole staff could just "no speak English".

The chain of secrecy about the project was maintained from the big cities in East where workers were recruited clear through to the delivery of these same workers on The Hill. The Alamos Bus stop was at Sena Plaza and people laden with luggage and youngsters clinging to their arms, frequently barged into offices of that Plaza and inquired, "Where do we go to work?" One of the earliest bits of Alamos lore was that of the dude Wac who had never been farther west than Albany, N. Y.; she chose the moment when The Hill bus was turning the highest point on the Jemez mountains to peek out—and fainted dead away.

Under these conditions of secrecy rumors multiplied like maggots in one of Mel Hagman's garbage cans. Gas warfare, rockets, jet propulsion, death rays and — atomic bombs — were among the guesses most frequently voiced. During the last Presidential campaign, Alamos—no foolin'—was sometimes a Republican internment camp.

In the early days of the project, even the "outside employes" who knew no more of what was going on than the Japs in the foxholes of Guadalcanal, were sworn never to reveal what they didn't know anyway, for the rest of their lifetime. Our own B. B. Dunne got tangled in the wringer for so much as mentioning that "there were a lot of scientists in town".

Then there was the time when the New York Daily was whipping up a Sunday feature on Nobel prize-winners in the U. S. It queried The New Mexican for a brief summary of what Prof X was doing now. The staff recognized the Alamos postoffice box number—that famous postal box where babies were born and to which whole crateloads of furniture assigned—but it was decided to give the professor a whirl anyway on the old "You can't shoot me for trying" principle. A letter went out to Professor X in which an interview was asked.

The next morning at 8:09—their watches must have been slow,—two guards jumped the cityroom. After a heap of protestations and avowals of innocence, it was agreed that the following telegram could be sent the News:

"Your man working for Mr Whiskers on extremely hush-hush project. No soap."

The telegram was delivered in New York by a Western Union boy flanked by a covey of guards. These men then began spilling all over the News cityroom like oranges out of a busted crate.

How, they wanted to know, did the News staff explain such Dick Tracy huggermugger stuff?

The News' difficulty was that the girl who had sent the telegram had gone on vacation and couldn't be reached. The News explained it after two clouded weeks in which, by report, you couldn't toss a cigaret in a wastepaper basket without setting fire to a guard.

The tantalizing little that Santa Feans knew about The Hill, only heightened their interest. There were the lights to be seen from miles away; there were the days when fires raged and smoked billowed in the mountains and always the mysterious explosions — (Lady Holmes moved to Tesuque and had moments when she thought she was back in bomb-shattered London!)

The payoff, however, came in the "Battle of the MPs". More than a year ago a boxing card was arranged in which the Santa Fe High athletes took on the Alamos MPs. The sluggers from The Hill must have been missing out on their vitamins or the Demons were packing an atomic punch because the MPs were knocked cold, two or three of them in one round and one punch practically.

Unfortunately for Mel Rhine and his Santa Fe MPs—as distinct from the Alamos MPs—soldiers read the sports pages and the next Saturday night, there was an epidemic of free-swinging in the bars and restaurants.

Frantically Rhine demanded that The New Mexican print an explanation that the one-round pushovers were decidedly NOT his MPs but he ran smack into the Alamos secrecy ban.

For hours Rhine sweated over a document which, by the time it complied with censorship requirements, rambled for no less than 700 words or so—and meant exactly nothing to anybody. It was a masterpiece of obfuscation. Of course, the boys were still swinging at the so-called "one-round MPs" for weeks before they discovered their mistake.

The Weather

New Mexico: Partly cloudy with widely scattered thunderstorms mostly over mountains during afternoon and evening; otherwise fair tonight and tomorrow; no important change in temperature.

City
High 90, low 56.

Airport
High 82, low 62

Today a modern laboratory complex sprawls over South Mesa replacing the wartime buildings.

after trinity

A crashing let-down followed the long months of intense technical effort and the climax of victory; the Laboratory faltered and very nearly perished. Much of the credit for holding it together goes to Norris Bradbury, the Laboratory's second and present director and the handful of men who shared his confidence in the facility's future.

Before the summer of 1945 had ended, a mass exodus from the Hill had begun. Many scientists, technicians and graduate students rushed to return to universities and industries from which they had been begged, borrowed or stolen for the wartime project. Many were lured away, and still others seriously tempted, by large salaries offered by universities attempting to rebuild their depleted technical staffs. In general, the Laboratory was staffed at the end of the war with people who were far from sure they wished to remain in Los Alamos.

For everyone there were some very large uncertainties. Neither the government nor the University of California had set down a plan for future operation of the Laboratory. The University had accepted the Los Alamos contract only as a patriotic gesture and there was no guarantee that the contract would continue. In the absence of national legislation on future use and control of atomic energy, there was little basis upon which to establish an appropriate policy for a laboratory whose initial mission was complete. Many thought the Laboratory would be abandoned. Others, suffering intense pangs of conscience, thought it ought to be —or that it should at least be turned over to basic and peaceful research.

All this was complicated by the question of whether or not a location on an isolated mesa, top in New Mexico was adequate or satisfactory as a peacetime location for a laboratory of any kind.

Furthermore, life on the Hill had never been easy and now, with the job finished, there was little incentive to endure it. The combination of an absentee contractor and Army administration of community and auxiliary services had aroused a state of antagonism and irritation that, for many people, could only be solved by leaving Los Alamos. By October, the Laboratory staff, which numbered 3,000 at its wartime peak, was nearing its all time low of only 1,000.

Then, adding to the confusion, Oppenheimer announced plans to return to his peacetime duties, and appointed Bradbury to take over as temporary director.

After the war, the Army-Navy E was presented to the Laboratory in special ceremonies at the Lodge. Gen. L. R. Groves made the presentation. Project Director J. Robert Oppenheimer is seated at far left.

An expert on conductivity of gases, properties of ions and atmospheric electricity, Bradbury had come to Los Alamos as an officer in the Naval Reserve after an outstanding academic career at Pomona, the University of California, Massachusetts Institute of Technology and Stanford, where he was a professor of physics. He was convinced that the nation would continue to need a laboratory for research into military applications of nuclear energy and that Los Alamos, now one of the world's best-equipped research laboratories, was the logical place for it. He gambled that the government would eventually agree with him.

Meeting with key staff members in October 1945, Bradbury laid his cards on the table. While awaiting legislation, he said, "we should set up the most nearly ideal project to study the use of nuclear energy." However, he continued, "we have an obligation to the nation never to permit it to be in a position of saying it has something that it has not. The project cannot neglect the stockpiling and development of atomic weapons during this period." The re-construction of a peacetime laboratory had begun.

In the spring of 1946, the Laboratory took over technical direction of Operation Crossroads at Bikini in the Marshall Islands. The historic test series supplied highly significant technical data on the effects of atomic weapons on naval vessels and gave the staff additional experience in the con-

duct of weapons tests. It also gave the Laboratory a concrete objective when it was most needed and proved the Laboratory's ability to conduct a major operation despite the loss of much of its experienced staff.

But still the situation in Los Alamos was uncertain. The final demoralizing blow had come in February of 1946 when the community water lines froze solid for weeks. Water was brought up from the Rio Grande in a procession of tank trucks and doled out in buckets and pans to grim-faced housewives. The disaster climaxed the bitter resentment of the system of Los Alamos community operation and hastened the exodus of still more unhappy people.

In May, Bradbury played his ace: he announced that, effective in September, the Laboratory would cease to pay the way home for terminating employees. Those who had been unable to make up their minds, quickly decided, and the staff stabilized, leaving only those who shared Bradbury's faith in Los Alamos.

The faith was confirmed often throughout the balance of 1946. In the spring, General Groves approved plans for construction of the Hill's first permanent housing, and prefabricated units were added as quick relief for the critical housing shortage.

The biggest boost came in August, when Congress passed the McMahon Act, establishing the Atomic Energy Commission and putting atomic energy under civilian control. As 1947 began, the Commission took over and the University of California agreed to continue operating the Laboratory. With the Commission establishing as its first priority "the stabilization and revitalization of the Los Alamos Scientific Laboratory," it became clear that Los Alamos would continue to play a key role in the nation's atomic energy program.

Although the Laboratory continued development of advanced fission weapons, it shortly embarked upon its second major mission—development of the hydrogen bomb.

Theoretical possibilities for a thermonuclear weapon, an idea born during a lunchtime discussion in early 1942, had been under study since the earliest days at Los Alamos by a special group headed by Edward Teller. Theoretically, the scientists knew, a fusion reaction was possible, but it required temperatures far higher than any previously created by man. With the success of the fission bomb, these high temperatures had been achieved. The thermonuclear bomb was now in the realm of practical possibility.

But major barriers were still unsurmounted. Once the cooperative efforts of Teller and Stanislaw Ulam made the necessary conceptual breakthrough, the Laboratory was able to launch an elaborate theoretical and experimental research program. The famous electronic brain, MANIAC, was built to handle the complex calculations of thermonuclear process, and the Laboratory went on a six-day week to get the job done. In November 1952, two months before the Laboratory's tenth anniversary, the world's first full-scale thermonuclear explosion shook the Pacific atoll of Eniwetok with the detonation of the Los Alamos device, "Mike."

Since that time, several dozen LASL fission and fusion devices have been tested in eight series of tests in the Pacific and in eight series, comprising 100 shots, conducted at the Nevada Test Site. With nuclear detonations in the atmosphere banned by the Limited Test Ban Treaty of 1963, Los Alamos now conducts a vigorous underground testing program in Nevada.

During the first decade, as it is today, the Laboratory's primary responsibility was development and improvement of nuclear weapons. However, in view of Bradbury's emphasis on "programs of fundamental research and development related to the problems of nuclear energy," it is not surprising only about half of the total Laboratory effort is now devoted to weaponry. Other programs cover a broad spectrum of investigation and development looking toward peaceful uses of atomic energy.

Beneficial exploitation of the atom at Los Alamos actually began as soon as the Laboratory was founded. Though the whole first purpose of the installation was to develop nuclear weapons, the nature of that purpose entailed a great deal of

World's first full-scale thermonuclear detonation took place November 1, 1952 in the Pacific. "Mike" shot used a LASL thermonuclear device and was conducted by LASL personnel.

LASL's Phoebus 1B reactor, one of a series of nuclear rocket propulsion reactors, sits on the test cell pad ready for the "girdle"—a radiation shield—to surround it. This photograph was taken through a door of the shed which protects the reactor from the elements.

purely scientific research. It required people and equipment fitted for much more than the creation of bombs.

In addition to the enriched-uranium reactor development before Trinity, Los Alamos reactors using entirely different fuel systems have been created. One of them—the world's first plutonium-fueled reactor and the first to rely on a fast-neutron fission chain—went into operation in 1946. In more recent years the Laboratory has developed a reactor using uranium phosphate fuel and another using molten plutonium. One present goal of the Los Alamos reactor program is to find good ways in which to design "breeder" reactors—reactors using neutron capture reactions to produce more fuel than they consume.

Los Alamos has also created the first nuclear rocket propulsion reactors (not intended to be flyable engines themselves, but designed to show the way toward the creation of propulsion systems far superior to those now in use).

Another peaceful program is Project Sherwood in which ways are being sought to harness the H-bomb fusion reaction and make it do useful work.

Scheduled for completion in 1971 is an 800 MeV proton accelerator which will produce pi mesons for the study of the atomic nucleus in ways not now possible. In addition, the meson facility may provide a valuable tool for cancer research.

The Laboratory's Health Research program has expanded from radiation effects studies to explorations in the field of molecular biology.

Over the years, while the Laboratory was making notable scientific advances, the community of Los Alamos itself was coming of age.

The AEC brought to Los Alamos—in the late 1940's—an ambitious $121 million plan for community expansion and laboratory relocation which put new, modern technical facilities on neighboring mesas, removing the unsightly old wooden structures and their high fences from the town's main street. A spacious, attractively landscaped shopping and community center was added. Schools and housing were built in a frantic effort to keep up with the need. A post office, library and medical center were added. In 1957, the gates came down and anybody who wanted to could come and go in the town.

Today, except for its rugged mountain setting, the community of bright green lawns and brilliant gardens looks just about like any suburban town. Its more than 16,000 residents enjoy an outstanding school system, a fast-growing shopping facility, plenty of recreation and three burgeoning residential subdivisions.

If Los Alamos is still not quite a "normal" community, it soon will be. In 1962, federal legislation was enacted to transfer commercial and residential property on the Hill from federal to private ownership and management. Nearly all property is now privately owned and final transfer of municipal operations and utilities to Los Alamos county was made in 1967.

Many changes have taken place on Pajarito Plateau during the past decades. Changes which have affected not only the community itself, but changes which have altered mankind's whole outlook on the world in which he lives. But one thing will not change: the Laboratory's adventurous spirit and the unmatched natural beauty of the setting which provides much of the inspiration for that spirit.

With an impressive record of accomplishments behind it, and its home town becoming what the AEC hoped in 1947 would be "a community satisfactory to scientists," the Laboratory can look to a promising future.